Cancer
Chameleon

Cancer
Chameleon

**HOW YOU AND YOUR CAREGIVER CAN TAKE
CONTROL OF YOUR CANCER TREK**

Andrew W. Trice Ph.D.

ISBN: 0997184604
ISBN 13: 9780997184600

Contents

Preface

'm happy, grateful, and lucky to be alive and well enough to write this book. Not everybody with cancer has the luxury of quality time to put together something like this. Based on the data for my particular cancer and stage, I gave myself about 18 months when I was first diagnosed; that time has long since passed, and though I have experienced a recurrence I am still living and loving life as a Cancer Chameleon, or at least trying my best. As soon as I realized that I had time left for something more than short "bucket list" items, I decided to write this book.

I sincerely hope that the experiences, thoughts, and research that went into this book will help you or your loved ones to navigate the cancer trek[1] more effectively. If I offend anyone by my bluntness, or my insight or advice doesn't resonate with you, you have my apologies in advance. One of the things that cancer taught me was to focus on the critical things in my life and get straight to the point, and that's what I've tried to do here.

I got the diagnosis of pancreatic cancer on May 24, 2013 at 4:38 p.m. (not that it was memorable or anything). As my treatment progressed and I had time to reflect on my own cancer trek and survival, I developed the audacity to believe that everything from my professional training (thinking through problems, breaking them down into bite-sized pieces, and presenting feasible solutions), personal temperament (objective

---

1   I use the term "cancer trek" rather than the more commonly used term "cancer journey" in this book, because "trek" implies a trip that is long and arduous in pursuit of a worthwhile goal, as opposed to "cancer journey" which also implies a trip, but could just as likely be a pleasant or neutral experience. For me, cancer is too challenging to deal with to be merely a journey.

and matter-of-fact, but creative and not entirely emotionally tone-deaf), and personal medical experience (the Whipple procedure, aka "Let's get our abdomen run over by a truck!", among many other adventures) could converge to produce a fantastic book about.....a cartoon reptile taking on a complex and deadly disease. I'm sure that's exactly what I told people when I was six and they asked me what I wanted to be when I grew up.

This book offers a way to approach the cancer trek and healing process, but contains almost no specific medical advice. If you're looking for news on cutting-edge treatments, advice on what doctor to go to, or tips on how to insert an IV for your ailing partner, this isn't the place. However, since it provides a broad set of perspectives for dealing with cancer, *Cancer Chameleon* will empower you to gain more control over the healing process, identify what other skills you'll need for coping with the trek's many challenges, and suggest how your support network can be most helpful.

I'd like to thank the countless people who assisted in so many indispensable ways in my healing and recovery process. There are far too many to list individually, but I must particularly acknowledge the amazingly skilled and capable medical staff at Johns Hopkins Hospital (especially Carol Judkins, R.N. and vaccine buddy; surgeon Dr. Christopher Wolfgang and his staff; and Dr. Lei Zheng, my oncologist); the staff at Virginia Cancer Specialists who handled my chemo regimens; and my internist Dr. Allen Horne, all of whom provided me with expert and compassionate medical care.

I'd also like to thank my incredible co-workers, who helped me decide on treatment strategies, drove me to endless radiation treatments, and reviewed much of this material; the loving clergy and congregation of Temple Rodef Shalom in Falls Church, Virginia; and my many friends, neighbors, fellow pancreatic cancer travelers, and fellow musicians for helping see me through diagnosis, surgery, treatment, and recovery.

In the family, my brothers Jeff and Mark and my brother- and sisters-in-law Bob and Allison Soffer, Carol Trice, and Maggie Trice, hung with me throughout this process with visits, hospital vigils, calls, prayers, and notes of encouragement. My mother-in-law Elaine Soffer has been a stalwart ally and supporter ever since I met my wife 33 years ago, and all the more so during my cancer trek. My daughters Julia and Laura handled their dad's experience with remarkable aplomb and kept things light for me.

My wife Sharon Soffer did more than anyone to love me, care for me, and encourage me to dig deep as I lost and gained back 30 pounds. Believe me when I say that I never had those 30 pounds to give in the first place—and that nobody but Sharon could find it harder to watch her husband lose weight in the face of such fantastic cooking. She also put up with me stealing the time from her to write this book.

Finally, our dog Draco has been the coolest and most affable post-treatment cancer workout partner you can imagine.

Many people also helped shape the content and focus of this book. Dr. Tracy Ginter Bushkoff and Julie Russell of Marymount University provided invaluable research on the resilience in cancer patients. The many readers of my blog posts gave me inspiration and feedback that encouraged me to share my words with a larger audience. Thanks also to my editor, Christina M. Frey, who pushed me to up my writing game, and to Mary Perry, Rabbi Stephanie Bernstein, Bill Patchak, Gary Lampal, Dave Hoard, Robin Madison, Lori Taylor, Stephanie Herman, Rachel Druck, and Elisa Joseph Anders for reviewing early versions of this manuscript. Mary Perry deserves special credit for her thorough copy editing. Finally, thanks to Jo Edwards for her great work on the cover design.

Aside from a few public figures and the family members and supporters whom I have named with their permission, everyone referenced in my original blog entries is kept anonymous to protect their privacy. My emails and blog entry excerpts appear almost exactly as originally written, with only light editing for clarity. Any errors in this text are of course my own.

Arlington, Virginia
January 2016

Dedications

A Pre-Operative Toast: "To Healing", composed by author shortly before Whipple surgery, June 2013

To all those loved ones who give us support and strength in the face of adversity—
   Spouses and families,
   Friends and neighbors,
   Colleagues and communities.

To all those special people who apply their skills, gifts, and experiences to repair our bodies and give us guidance, comfort, and hope--
   Doctors and nurses,
   Therapists and clergy,
   Confidants and fellow travelers.

To all those who generously keep us in their thoughts and prayers--
   No matter their traditions or beliefs,
   No matter their connection to us,
   But out of their shared and genuine compassion and caring towards us.

And to all of these things that somehow combine with the workings of our own bodies and spirits to produce that mysterious thing we call "healing."

To healing!

Also to my parents, Joan and Ted, who didn't live to see me go through this, but gave me the tools and values I needed to handle it.

And, of course, to Sharon.

I like being like a chameleon who transforms himself with each role.-- Oscar Isaac, actor

We are chameleons, and our partialities and prejudices change place with an easy and blessed facility, and we are soon wonted to the change and happy in it. -- Mark Twain, humorist and author

We are like chameleons, we take our hue and the color of our moral character, from those who are around us. -- John Locke, philosopher and physician

Prologue

May 2013

Early 2013 was a very busy time for me. My parents died in January, four days apart, and the next four months were a flurry of grief, estate settlement, and day-to-day living. I was also determined to move forward with two very important priorities: holding my long-planned fiftieth birthday celebration and concert in mid-May and moving into our new dream house with my wife Sharon and daughters Julia and Laura later that spring.

In early May, a few weeks before my birthday, I experienced mild digestive symptoms and fatigue that seemed a little bit out of the ordinary. Being so busy, I just ignored them, but right after the house settlement and the concert I made an appointment to see my general practitioner. He did some blood tests and discovered that my liver panels were high. We made an appointment for an ultrasound the next day, and in the meantime I did a little bit of hypochondriatic searching on the Internet to understand what I might be facing. Reaction to a medication? Most likely. Gallbladder surgery needed? Maybe. Pancreatic cancer? Nah, I was too young and healthy for that.

CHAPTER 1

Your Cancer Trek: The Rewards of Regaining Control

O
kay, so you or someone close to you has cancer, maybe a very serious diagnosis. As a fellow traveler, I'm truly sorry and can empathize with what's going through your mind, and many of the negative experiences, thoughts, and emotions you have had. Right now, you may be numb, panicked, overwhelmed, hurting, bone-tired, or angry as hell--or some combination of these. To whatever degree, cancer has taken over your life. It's not anything you had a say in, yet it could shorten the quality and quantity of your (or your loved one's) future. And that's just unfair and a bummer—full stop.

You have every right to feel this way—it would be hypocritical of me to suggest otherwise, because I have certainly done my share of wailing and venting to family, friends, and professionals. And the challenges aren't going to end now; they will be ongoing, making the cancer experience a trek with many hardships, not just an ordinary journey.

But the unfairness and helplessness of it all is only one layer of the story, and probably not the most interesting layer either. In fact, wherever you are physically, emotionally, or spiritually right now, there is hope and the opportunity to regain some measure of control over your trek from here, and to improve the quality (and perhaps the quantity) of life that lies ahead. And it has less to do with the medical layer of the trek than with what goes on in your head and how you and those around you approach and act on your situation. Because a trek is not only challenging, it is also an opportunity to pursue many worthwhile goals along the way.

This book presents a range of tools you can use to permit you, empower you, and guide you to design and implement your own "control system" across the multiple layers of your cancer trek. To do this, you'll need to approach and tackle that trek from a variety of perspectives; just sticking to one would make you inflexible and more fragile physically and emotionally. Independent of any particular cancer type, prognosis and treatments you're facing, I'd venture to say that almost all of the important issues you're wrestling with lie in one of three near-universal questions:

1. *How do I cope?* (*Typical feeling: "Oh, s*!t!")* Cancer poses many "in the moment" challenges. How do you deal with overwhelming anxiety about the prognosis? Physical pain that limits your energy? A daunting task related to medical care or finances? A big decision about which treatment(s) to try? A sudden gap in your ability to attend to those you normally care for? In these situations, "Take it one day at time" is good philosophical advice, but you may desperately need more specific guidance on what you can do to cope better during in that particular moment.

2. *How do I manage?* (*Typical feeling: "Ugh, sigh.."*) Cancer is also a big project that can drag on for months or years—akin to managing an organization ("Cancer, Inc."?). There may be ongoing activities in research and development (new treatments or diets to investigate), strategy (aggressive treatment vs. more conservative treatment), public relations (communication with a support network or medical professionals), operations (medication and pain management or transportation arrangements), human resources (volunteer management, care for the caregiver), and finance and legal (insurance issues or estate planning)—and many more.

3. *How do I live?* (*Typical feeling: "Why me, and what now?"*) Finally, cancer raises deep questions about the meaning and purpose of life. You may feel the urge to reflect on what all of this existential struggle is for and decide how it's going to affect your life. For example, how can you preserve your sense of self now that you or yours are living with cancer? Do you want to spend your time differently in the future? What kind of person do you want to be now and how do you want to be remembered? Do you feel compelled to give something back or share your experience with others?

With indispensable help from my family, friends, and other supporters, I've been tackling these questions head-on since I was diagnosed with pancreatic cancer in

2013—and I've learned that taking a systematic approach to them can increase your sense of control over the fundamental cancer trek issues and yield many rewards that make it well worth the extra effort and the challenges (Table 1).

Question	Rewards of Control System	Challenges
How do I cope?	-Successful navigation through crises	-Improving self-regulation
	-Sound decisions made under stress or time pressure	-Focusing attention when under stress
	-Mindfulness and calmness	
How do I manage?	-Capacity to prevent some crises	-Getting organized
	-Feelings of effectiveness	-Setting up processes
	-More time to heal and enjoy life	-Delegating effectively
How do I live?	-A meaningful life and legacy	-Clarifying goals
	-The ability to maintain authenticity	-Making hard trade-offs
		-Owning the trek

Table 1: Rewards and challenges of a cancer control system

Why bother learning some new system—isn't putting one foot in front of the other while living with the disease hard enough? It is hard, but we can employ a metaphor to help make it easier. Specifically, we'll use the metaphor of a chameleon that is able to change its colors. A chameleon is an appropriate metaphor because of all of the cool things it does to adapt to its environment—defend itself against predators, self-regulate for heat or cold, give off social signals, even see multiple things at once. In short, the chameleon is successful because it can dial up or dial down the different color combinations it plays to adapt to its environment.

Like the chameleon, there are many different colors (roles) and tints (virtues) that you can use to gain much more control over your environment (all of the crappy stuff cancer can throw at you). Using these "color roles" and tints within a larger control system has been my most effective tool in navigating my cancer trek, and I hope it can help you too.

The control system is all about judicious application of the different color roles. We'll be going through the color roles in detail in subsequent chapters, but to give you a flavor for what a color role is and some of subtleties of applying it, let's take the well-known idea of the Cancer Warrior, one of the color roles we'll discuss later. The Cancer Warrior fights the disease by persevering no matter how hard it is, and bearing the pain, trials, and indignity of cancer with great strength. The Cancer Warrior just doesn't let up or give in; in this color role, you keep defying the cancer for as long as it takes.

I have the greatest respect for the Cancer Warrior color role; I've needed to employ it myself at times, though I don't pretend my trek has been as tough as many others'. But what about when you just want to forget about your cancer, are in remission, or find yourself facing end-of-life issues? At those times, you may want to dial back the Warrior and play some other color roles too. But where exactly is that line between when to hold on and when to let go? The answer may be different for every person.

As you'll see, there are complexities that apply to the color roles generally as well. First, the color roles are often interconnected. Just as the medical treatments used for cancer often employ multiple approaches that complement each other (e.g., radiation may kill cancer cells at the initial tumor site, while chemo may kill cancer cells throughout the body), the different color roles can have complementary purposes in your cancer control system. For example, if the Warrior is about fighting, other color roles can give the Warrior the emotional or logistical support to continue fighting. At the same time, just as medical treatments can also conflict with each other or have undesirable side effects (e.g., radiation can weaken the immune system and make chemo harder to do) so too can the color roles conflict. The ethic of Warrior is to fight and hold on, but this may conflict with the need to accept and let go that is appropriate at other times.

Sometimes the connection is even more subtle. If you do a good job proactively managing the disease and its treatments, you will likely spend less time coping with crises, free up more time to pursue meaningful activities, or even somewhat reduce the need to play the Warrior. Likewise, if you have time to reflect on what type of person you want to be and what is truly important, you may stress out less and find yourself less upset about conditions that might have triggered a crisis reaction before.

Additionally, the color roles are played by a team. Cancer is too overwhelming an experience to expect that any one person can do all of the heavy lifting. To fulfill the different color roles, the key caregiver(s) and a larger support network usually augment what the person with cancer brings to the table, and back fill what that person can't or won't take on. This raises a whole host of leadership issues and relationship dynamics in the cancer trek; these will be addressed in a separate chapter as well as throughout the individual color role chapters.

Finally, the color roles must be customized. Your cancer trek is unique; no two people going through this will have the same prognosis, level of support, personal skills, or temperament. Even within your own trek, things inevitably change. Your treatment intensity waxes and wanes. Your energy level goes up and down. Your prognosis and priorities shift. And therefore your inclination to employ any given color role, how much you fulfill a color role yourself or look to others to fulfill it, are all yours to decide and adjust. All of the color roles are there to provide a toolbox of useful perspectives for dealing with the cancer trek more effectively, but in the end you have to decide which ones to emphasize and when.

Even though you might think the complexity of these color roles place even more burdens upon you, the color roles are also a rich source of potential meaningfulness, and greater rewards. These can include using the color roles together so they help you heal better, getting better help from your support network, and tailoring your cancer trek to what feels right for you. To the degree that you can grasp and apply these principles, you will be in a great position to make your cancer trek your own and have the best experience possible.

The concept of the Cancer Chameleon will be most valuable to those who will survive or even thrive for a significant period after diagnosis, and who spend months or years in what I call the "cancer jungle" of multiple types of various treatments and uncertain prognosis[2]. It will also be useful for caregivers helping them at the various stages of their trek.

The small minority of people who are diagnosed with cancer and either have a quick treatment and cure or conversely, receive a terminal diagnosis, will still benefit from

---

2 According to Cancer Facts and Figures 2014 (American Cancer Society) the 5-year relative survival rate (i.e. the percentage of people who did not die of cancer within 5 years of being diagnosed) for cancer diagnosed between 2003 and 2009 in the USA is 68%, and will probably be even higher for cases diagnosed since then. See American Cancer Society, Cancer Facts and Figures 2014 (Atlanta: American Cancer Society, 2014), accessed October 22, 2015, http://www.cancer.org/acs/groups/content/@research/documents/webcontent/acspc-042151.pdf.

the color roles presented here; it's just that they may not have the need or the time to execute all of the color roles to same extent. In these situations, either the cancer is not so distressing or transformational that it requires a wide range of coping strategies, or the condition is so serious and incapacitating that the patient moves directly to end-of-life issues.

There is another important limitation, or at least assumption, about applying the Cancer Chameleon principles. Generally, I assume that the cancer patient, the family, and the wider support network are generally functional and have no debilitating preexisting mental health issues. This book cannot teach you to repair or rebuild broken relationships, change family dynamics, or treat mental health conditions; that scope would simply be too ambitious and mental health professionals can do a much better job at those things than I can do in a book written by a layperson. The most I can do is to identify situations in which professional counseling would be in order.

A cancer diagnosis and trek is stressful enough to challenge even very healthy relationships, and while I suggest ways that caregivers and support networks can help one another and reduce their stress, I acknowledge that the job is much tougher if the basic relationships aren't at least reasonably solid to begin with. From the accounts I have read of the cancer treks of others, I have seen many poignant stories in which there is there is some genuine caring by one or more parties, but the underlying relationships have historically been problematic, and this has made the cancer trek much, much harder. As I have been blessed with wonderful family relationships and connections with many friends and communities, I felt I could contribute the most by documenting what can be done starting from a baseline of some relationship stability and strength.

Please view this book as a resource guide for making the best possible use of the different color roles, however much they resonate with you. And feel free to jump around the content in whichever way best suits your particular needs. Even if you're tired and overwhelmed, I hope you'll find some "quick wins" to help you on your cancer trek.

Here's the roadmap for where we're going. Chapter 2 introduces the color roles and the "palette" of very useful skills and perspectives you can enact to meet the demands of your cancer trek. Chapter 3 addresses the critical contribution of the caregiver in enabling a better experience for both the patient and themselves. Chapters 4-12 describe the color roles in detail, and how to implement them in a variety of situations; we'll identify key tasks, strengths, pitfalls, and best practices associated with each.

Chapter 13 explains the skills and attitudes, or color "tints," that will be useful to you no matter which color role you're enacting. Chapter 14 provides examples of how the color roles and tints might be applied to support your specific cancer trek, and Chapter 15 offers concluding thoughts.

Let's continue by introducing the diverse set of chameleon colors and the roles they correspond to. Each color role is a powerful tool you can use to transform your perspective on the cancer trek into something positive. Once you become familiar with the color roles, you'll see how they can help you rapidly adapt to whatever cancer throws your way. You'll be on the road to becoming a Cancer Chameleon.

CHAPTER 2

Color Roles: The Cancer Chameleon Palette

C hameleons take on shades that are within the range of colors that their species has evolved to possess, and these hues can include everything from aquamarine blue to pale pink and even patterned stripes and spots.[3]

You are always a work in progress, and as long as you are alive the canvas is never finished, as there is always more color on the palette.[4]

3   Remy Melina, "Chameleon Color Change Isn't All about Hiding," *Live Science*, March 28, 2011, http://www.livescience.com/33159-chameleon-color-change-isnt-all-about-hiding.html.

4   Bernie Siegel, MD, Author of *Love, Medicine, and Miracles*. Bernie Siegel, *Love, Medicine, and Miracles: Lessons about Self-Healing from a Surgeon's Experience with Exceptional Patients* (New York: Harper & Row, 1986).

In the course of my own cancer trek, I've identified nine color roles that have been very useful to me in navigating my cancer trek more effectively. Each of them has brought something different to the table for me. They've given me a diverse skill set that, when carefully and flexibly applied by my support network and me, have enhanced my cancer trek.

Similarly, that goofy-looking chameleon guy above got where he is (smiling on a precarious-looking branch) because he's got so many colors going, and he's able to change them at will in response to whatever new situation in which he finds himself.

Because to be sure, cancer is going to place you in a lot of very challenging situations— physical, mental, emotional, and spiritual. To respond effectively and strike back at cancer with all the tools you can get, you first need to internalize what they are, but more importantly what they do which is to enable yourself to transform yourself in some empowering way. Each of the color roles moves you

From a particular state or sense of feeling out of control,
   To a state of being in better control.

Figure 1 shows the list of nine color roles[5], the transformation each can enable for you, and the typical situations in which they are used.

—✸✸✸—

Crisis Manager enables you to transform **from** feeling overwhelmed
   to focusing on a plan to handle the challenge or situation.

Use Crisis Manager when you need to make quick decisions about treatment options or medical care, or in other stressful or time-sensitive situations that interact with the illness, such as dealing with a disability or the needs of another family member. Choosing how to manage the more stressful or urgent situations can bring you an important measure of control.

---

5 I chose the colors for the roles based on what different colors have generally signified in Western history and psychological or biological research, but don't think there's anything immutable about the choices I made.

9

Publicist enables you to transform **from** being *closed* to sharing the realities of your cancer trek,

> **to** being *open* about the disease and the help you need.

Use Publicist when you want to communicate with others to describe your situation, whether a diagnosis, a treatment, your morale, or your needs. In this color role, you choose what to share, when to share, with whom to share, and through what medium to share. You're in control of the information flow by keeping everyone appropriately informed and facilitating the support you need.

Actor enables you to transform **from** feeling *marginalized* from mainstream life and social activities,

> **to** *engaging* with the outside world in meaningful and authentic ways.

Use Actor when you want to behave as if the cancer doesn't exist or reclaim a sense of self beyond the disease. When you enact this color role, you're able to go about your daily business, to the extent you are physically able, leaving the cancer deep in the background and effectively ignored.

Warrior enables you to transform **from** feeling *intimidated* by the cancer and its threat to health or life,

> **to** *fighting* actively against the disease.

Use Warrior when you want to battle the disease by dint of will and personal strength, showing your toughness and perseverance in the face of cancer's physical and emotional challenges. In this color role, you may bear pain, discomfort, or emotional or spiritual challenges without complaint, and push forward in the face of any difficulty to accomplish your survival mission.

Patient enables you to transform **from** being *wounded* by the cancer or its attendant treatments,

> **to** participating in the *healing* process, physically or emotionally.

Use Patient when you are receiving or recovering from treatment, whether it's a doctor's visit or checkup, an outpatient procedure, hospitalization, or chemo or radiation. This color role allows you to acknowledge the disease but focus on following the professionals' advice and permitting yourself to rest and heal.

Scout enables you to transform **from** *trudging* through the cancer trek one difficult step at a time,
   to *navigating* diagnosis, treatment, and recovery by evaluating different courses of action.

Use Scout to plan your treatment sequence, research future treatment options, and understand how cancer may interact with other aspects of your life. This color role emphasizes a proactive approach; by evaluating possibilities, you can plan for future lifestyle needs and accommodations.

Philosopher enables you to transform **from** having simply *survived* (!) the cancer for a period of time,
   to *clarifying* your life priorities for the future.

Use Philosopher to step back and reassess your life in light of the illness. This color role may involve reflective activities (e.g., journaling, retreats, or meditation) and allow you to evaluate and reorder your life priorities, sometimes drastically.

Guru enables you to transform **from** a period of *self-focus* due to the ongoing challenges of the disease,
   to a readiness to *contribute* to a purpose higher than yourself.

Use Guru when you want to turn your survival into something greater, now that you have survived this far in the cancer trek. Through this color role you may provide encouragement and advice to those going through a similar experience, or embrace some broader cause that is important to you, thereby expanding your circle of influence and your ability to make the trek about more than just survival.

Mortal enables you to transform **from** being *terrified* of disability and death,
   to *accepting* a range of possible outcomes.

Use **Mortal** to face disability and death head-on, acknowledge that your life is limited, and grant that the cancer may shorten it or affect it long-term, perhaps dramatically. This color role allows you to make peace with what has happened and, in the last phase of life, deal with the process of "letting go."

Figure 1: Color Role List

Collectively, the color roles form a "palette" that you, as a Cancer Chameleon (hereafter, CC) can draw from to enrich and improve your cancer trek. Each of these color roles is critically important at different points, but they are not meant to be used in isolation; in fact, because each color role represents only a partial truth of dealing with cancer, relying too much on one color role may trip you up if the situation demands something different. In the end, each CC must learn to adapt by changing the mix of color roles they enact as the trek unfolds.

For example, think about the way changing the mix of the color roles can help the CC address the three big issues: how to cope, how to manage, and how to live. As Table 2 shows, some color roles are more helpful than others when facing a particular question, and the most successful CC's are those who can apply the right color roles at different times during the trek. If you're pressed for time, you may want to focus on the color roles most valuable to the fundamental issue you're concerned with.

Color Role	Usefulness for Coping ("Now")	Usefulness for Managing ("Project")	Usefulness for Living ("Life/Legacy")
Crisis Manager	High	Medium	Low
Publicist	Medium	High	Medium
Actor	Medium	Low	High
Warrior	High	Low	Medium
Patient	High	Medium	Low
Scout	Low	High	Medium
Philosopher	Low	Medium	High
Guru	Low	Medium	High
Mortal	Medium	Low	High

Table 2: Relative Usefulness of Color Roles for the Big Cancer Trek Issues

The beauty of the palette is that the CC can blend color roles at different times to assume more control and blend the color roles to work the best within the environment you face at any particular moment.

For example, if you read down the first column, you'll see that combining Crisis Manager, Warrior, and Patient—which all have potentially high value for coping—is a powerful formula for dealing with an immediate, urgent challenge. Similarly, blending Scout and Publicist can help manage the longer-term cancer "project", and Actor combined with the last three color roles works well to help the CC build a meaningful life and legacy.

There is a further nuance to applying the color roles, and that refers to the manner in which you fulfill them. For example, someone with a good sense of humor who is passionate about life and skilled at mindfulness is going to do better than someone with the opposite personality traits. I call these qualities (which benefit you no matter what the situation) "tints", and we will discuss them briefly in conjunction with the color roles as we proceed, and then in more depth in their own chapter.

Finally, enacting a color role at any given time doesn't have to be a "go big or do nothing" proposition; you can obtain benefits from playing that color role just a little bit. Even if some of the initial color role descriptions don't resonate for you, either because you don't see the need for them or can't imagine how you could perform them, remember that your needs and priorities change as you go through the cancer trek. For example, if life is miserable at the moment because of emotional shock or physical discomfort and you are in pure coping mode, that can shift once you have a treatment plan, treatment starts, or a treatment is over; and conversely, bumps in the road and crises can occur after periods of relatively serene living.

If you can't see how you could ever be physically or emotionally capable of performing a color role, others on your team might be able to help you do it or even take it over entirely.

In the next chapter we'll talk about how your team– most specifically your primary caregiver(s)– can think about and apply these color roles themselves, effectively helping their CC gain control yet preserving their own sense of self.

CHAPTER 3

Caregivers, Welcome to the Chameleon Dance

*M*y caregiver mantra is to remember: the only control you have is over the changes you choose to make.[6]

If you're a caregiver to the CC, this chapter is for you—and for your CC. Both of you have been rudely plunked down into the "Chameleon Dance" that is the cancer trek—a dance you didn't want to be invited to, but which you need to make the best of. No matter your prior relationship with each other--spouses, partners, parent and child, or close friends—there are big changes in store for both of you. But as we'll see, at least you get to pick the kind of dance(s) you'll do together.

First things first: this whole trek may feel just as crappy for you as a caregiver as for your CC. Seeing my wife in distress is as bad as having physical pain myself (and vice versa). As a caregiver, you face the same set of big issues; you too need to cope with the day-to-day challenges, help manage your loved one's cancer trek as it extends, and grapple with redefining life in light of the CC's illness.

Then there is the dance dimension of it all: when do you lead the CC in the dance, when do you allow the CC to lead, when do you let somebody else cut in on your dance with the CC, and when do you just take a rest break or dance with others, even

---

6 Nancy L., Kriseman, *The Mindful Caregiver: Finding Ease in the Caregiver Journey* (Lanham, MD: Rowman & Littlefield, 2014).

though the CC is your first partner of choice? As dedicated as you are to your CC, you have to have some autonomy too.

Like your CC, you can enact color roles that give you more control over your part of the trek and how you mesh with the CC. You will face an ongoing set of choices in which you'll need to decide whether to step up to or step back from the process, to sacrifice or preserve yourself, and to manage the risks of intruding on the CC's autonomy versus the risks of making them feel abandoned.

You will also determine how much to engage with the CC's disease and when you should seek help from others in the wider support network. You should have full permission to make these choices without guilt, but conscious of the trade-offs you are making. This chapter will give you a way to think about these trade-offs, and later chapters on the individual color roles will offer more specific guidance on what you can do to enact the color roles and encourage others to help fulfill them too.

Generally a caregiver can engage with a color role in one of four modes: they can *fulfill* it for the CC, *partner* with the CC on enacting the color role, *support* the CC's lead, or *stand by* and let the CC or others do it. But don't think of any of these modes as good or bad, responsible or irresponsible. To successfully navigate the cancer trek with your CC, you'll probably need all four at different times.

- *Fulfill: "I've got this, honey!"* You should fulfill a color role when the CC is either unwilling or unable to do it themselves *and* you have the will and the capability to enact it. For example, a CC who is relatively incapacitated from exhaustion or a hospital stay probably can't act as their own Publicist, but a caregiver with the desire and the communication skills can do that job for them.
  Upside: You'll make your biggest contribution to the CC by taking over where they cannot.
  Downside: You may risk feeling burned out or put-upon.
- *Partner: "I'm all in with you, darling".* You should *partner* with the CC on a color role when you both have the willingness and capability to perform the color role, and believe you can do a better job at it if you're working together. For instance, both of you could ask questions at medical appointments (Patient), do independent research on treatment possibilities (Scout), and

discuss pros and cons of different options to quickly reach a joint decision (Crisis Manager).

Upside: You'll strengthen your relationship with each other and improve the quality of your joint cancer trek decisions.

Downside: You may find making complex decisions by consensus time-consuming and even frustrating.

- *Support: "I've got your back, I just can't move your whole body".* You should *support* the CC's lead in playing a color role when you have limited time, ability, or willingness to enact the color role, but can still facilitate the color role's execution. For example, you could share inspirational materials to help the CC enact the Warrior, be the scribe at the Patient's appointments, or drive the CC to social events where the CC can play the color role of Actor.

  Upside: You can help the CC without having to own the color role.

  Downside: Because support mode can include activities that are necessary but not unique to your skill set, it may be more appropriate to outsource such tasks to others if you already have a full plate.

- *Bystander: "I need to let you, your buds, or the pros do their thing".* You should *stand by* and let the CC or others enact the color role in all other cases:

  - When the CC is performing it competently already. For example, the CC may be a good Publicist, enjoy doing it, and be well enough to perform the color role.

  - When it's a priority to the CC but not to you (and a discretionary activity). For example, if the CC elects to be a Guru for a cause that you don't feel connected to, and you shouldn't be required to engage.

  - When others (e.g., friends or professionals) who are available can do it better. For example, the CC might engage a sibling who is a good writer to be their Publicist, or seek outside counseling to explore their Philosopher or Mortal issues.

  - When you need to distance yourself from a color role to preserve your identity or (at least temporarily) avoid becoming emotionally or physically overwhelmed. For example, you may engage respite care to support the CC Patient at home to keep yourself from breaking down.

  - Keep in mind that some of the color roles inherently limit how much you can do as a caregiver; for example, no one can tell another how to live their life (that is, fulfill the Philosopher for them), let alone how to accept disability or death (fulfill the Mortal)

Upside: Being a bystander frees up your physical and emotional energy to have your own life too.

Downside: By not participating, you can lose some control over how things are done; you may also feel guilty if things go poorly (whether that's appropriate or not)

There's a reason why I listed so many situations in which standing by is the right mode—to emphasize that you should not feel guilty about stepping back from certain color roles and letting others handle them. Sometimes for your own sanity it's wise to seek more help on the color roles than you might first be inclined to (and to get the CC on board with that idea as well). Your life may be very different for a while and you will need to jointly change your priorities and expectations to align with that new reality; just because you are capable of doing something under normal circumstances doesn't mean that you should be doing it now.

Finally, anticipate the stress the cancer trek places on your relationship and the additional expectations the CC may have of you. Even if the CC is profoundly grateful for the help you are providing, occasionally there will be mismatches between what they want from you and what you want to do for them with respect to any color role. The CC may need more than you are capable of giving, and feel abandoned if you don't do it. The CC may want less than what you'd like to give, and feel intruded upon when you provide it. One of you may obsess about things that the other thinks are trivial. You may disagree about proper courses of action with respect to treatments (Crisis Manager or Scout), communication with others (Publicist), legacy planning (Mortal), and more. The best solution is to work hard on communicating well with each other about your insights, needs, priorities, and worries (and I encourage you to vent separately to friends or professionals too). This includes discussing the grim possibilities about where the cancer may eventually lead.

As a caregiver you will be doing a complex dance with your CC during the cancer trek. The contours of your relationship will change, perhaps drastically, as you find yourself encountering new stresses, doing entirely new activities, picking up the slack in pre-existing commitments, adjusting your level of engagement with the CC, and learning to be flexible and creative about how you handle things as the disease and treatments run their course.

I'm biased, but I can't think of a better exemplar for an excellent, loving, and balanced caregiver than my wife Sharon. Here's some of the wonderful traits she continues to live out while caring for me:

—⊗—

Sharon Is Awesome

posted by Andrew Trice, Tuesday, November 12, 2013

Everything going well here at the moment, I'm regaining some stamina after radiation and feeling good; the only sticking point is that I would still like to gain more weight. I tried putting lead sinkers in my pants to fool the scales, but it didn't work. However, the heavy diet of Sharon's cooking is still very satisfying.

Speaking of Sharon, I wanted to take some time during this little inter-regnum between treatments to focus on the critical role a supportive spouse or partner plays in the healing process. Some of my more philosophical previous posts have covered various cross-cutting non-medical issues as the attitude of the patient, the role of music, and the interpretation of statistics. Relationships are a critical driver and influencer on how you fare that deserves its own treatment, so to speak.

I just finished a new book entitled "In Sickness As In Health: Helping Couples Cope with the Complexities of Illness." Given our situation, I was curious about the topic both for its own sake and also to see if it could help us benchmark how we are doing and what we could be doing better. There are many good nuggets in the book, but what struck me the most was how Sharon already exemplified many of the "best practices" of the "well spouse" in the relationship. For instance:

"Positive Coping:" This is defined as being able to focus on practical prob-lem-solving while at the same time acknowledging the seriousness of the spouse's illness and providing him with emotional support. Sharon is both a tough cookie and also the person you want in your corner when your times are tough.

"Balancing Mutuality and Autonomy:" Illness places a lot of demands on the well spouse; both increased responsibility and increased anxiety about your part-ner. I think this is where the well spouse actually has the tougher job. At the same time, you have to be able to define yourself as someone other than just a caregiver, or you will go crazy or burn out. Sharon has done this superbly, continuing to work, run the house, meet with friends, etc. while still looking after my needs.

"Speaking the Unspeakable:" From the beginning, we have managed to talk about all dimensions of my illness very openly, from the best-case to the worst-case scenario and everything in between. No wishful thinking or avoidance of harsh possibilities. I know it takes a backbone of steel to discuss these things, but Sharon has the strength and practicality to take it on with me.

"Constructing a Helping Community:" An illness like this is too much to handle on your own. But to get help from others, you have to be able to "open the kimono" and figure out how to get others to help, even if your natural impulse is to be private and deal with things on your own. I was very impressed that Sharon got on board with Lotsa Helping Hands site quickly, allowed me to share some pretty personal information via my emails, and figured out ways to enable people to help her. In addition, we both are employing a range of trusted advisors in a structured way to help us cope with the illness individually and as a family.

You might have seen recent media reports about how people who are married have statistically better outcomes in recovering from illness. Having Sharon makes me understand why this assertion is not at all a stretch.

—◦◦◦—

The color role chapters that follow will give you perspectives and practical suggestions for being an effective caregiver without losing your identify. Each chapter has a specific section ("Caregiver Connections") that will give you practical ideas on how to engage with the CC and perform in different modes against the specific color roles. At the same time, this material may give the CC insight on the dilemmas their caregivers face and suggest how the CC can make life easier for them (even if we CCs are needy whiners more than we'd like to admit).

Now let's dive into the individual color roles, beginning with a short guide on what a color role's pieces are and how you can find color role information quickly.

Quick Guide to the Color Roles and Tints

To make it easier for you to access and apply the information in this book in bite-sized chunks, each of the color role chapters has a common structure.

A typical color role chapter looks like this:

Color Role at a Glance: A table that provides a quick overview of the color role, including

- The *key transformation* it enables
- The *color* and its symbolic significance
- A brief *description* of the color role
- The situations in which it is *most applicable*
- The *benefits of, risks of neglecting,* and *risks of overdoing* the color role

How the Color Role Gives You Control: A breakdown of the color role in action, often illustrated by outside research and my own experience. This section shows you why the color role is important and the difference it can make in your trek.

How You Staff the Color Role: An outline of the skills and capabilities you need to fulfill the color role, and guidance on when and whether you should do the color role yourself or use others (caregiver, support network, or professionals) to do it.

Color Role and Tint Interactions: A guide to which color roles or tints are useful in conjunction with the main color role in the chapter, and which color roles are potentially in conflict with it (akin to Chinese horoscope compatibility guides: "Rabbit: Marry the Rat. Avoid the Monkey"). Tints are explored in more depth later, so feel free to jump ahead to Chapter 13 and learn more about a tint if you'd like to understand it apart from the context of a particular color role.

Caregiver Connections: A section devoted to the particular concerns of the caregivers, including where conflicts might arise and how to deal with them, and how the CC and caregiver might best support and reinforce one another's efforts in enacting the color role.

Quick Wins: Simple, positive things you can do to enact the color role, scoped by approximately how much time you have available. If you don't know where start with the color role, or have extremely limited time, this section is for you.

What Good Color Role Players Do: A broader best practices section with tips and tricks to keep in mind as you fulfill the color role.

Further Reading: References for those who want to explore a color role in more depth.

I have also interspersed some blog entries and personal reflections from my own cancer trek to give you further examples. However, this book is structured primarily as a self-help toolkit, an "equipping" book rather than a "commiserating" or "inspiring" book; the memoir aspect is more for illustration than to hold me up as any kind of a role model (pardon the pun). I'd rather help you survive and heal better than give you a good impression of me.

That said, let's continue by discussing the first color role that comes into play when the CC first discovers that there is something very different about their health than what they thought.

CHAPTER 4

The **Crisis Manager** Color Role: How Do I Survive?

A n excited chameleon might turn red by fully expanding all his erythrophores, blocking out the other colors beneath them.[7]

If you notice that a veiled chameleon instantly takes on a darker coloring, it often means that he is either shocked or in defensive mode.[8]

- **Crisis Manager at a Glance**
  - *Key Transformation:* from feeling *overwhelmed*, to *focusing* on a plan to handle the current challenge or situation.
  - *Color:* **Red** (think: urgency and danger)
  - *Description:* Marshal resources and information to make sound, critical decisions, and meet urgent needs
  - *Most applicable when*: initially diagnosed or in need of urgent physical, spiritual, or mental care
  - *Benefits:* Focuses attention at a critical point; forces you to make decision and move forward
  - *Risks of neglecting:* Lost opportunities, uninformed decisions, and bad outcomes
  - *Risks of overdoing:* Exhaustion, poor decisions made in reactive mode

---

7 Mary Bates, "How Do Chameleons Change Colors?," *Wired*, April 11, 2014, http://www.wired.com/2014/04/how-do-chameleons-change-colors/.

8 Naomi Milburn, "Identifying a Veiled Chameleon's Color and Mood," Pets on Mom.me, accessed October 22, 2015, http://animals.pawnation.com/identifying-veiled-chameleons-color-mood-5712.html.

How Crisis Manager Gives You Control

There are times in the cancer trek when it fills up the entire screen of your life. When you get the diagnosis, depending on its severity and your temperament, the feeling may be so all-consuming that afterward you may not even fully remember what it was like. There is no "right" way to process this information: numbness, shock, anger, incapacitation, or tears, or any number of other reactions are normal, and maybe even necessary. You don't know how you're going to survive all this. You are in crisis.

However, the sooner you can move from shock and despair into action mode, the more effective you can be. To navigate through and beyond the crisis, you (or someone in your support network) will need to turn on what I call the "inner EMT pose," the calm, authoritative, rational approach to problem-solving that an effective crisis response requires. The EMT must read the situation, identify the problem that needs immediate attention, and work from there until the patient is stabilized. There is only so much time for second-guessing; they must focus, decide, and then "move out" to treat the condition.

Similarly, the Crisis Manager's job is to bring together the best available information on the disease and patient in order to make important, urgent decisions, then marshal the resources needed to carry out those decisions—all under some time pressure.

By helping you think through the situation and prioritize, the Crisis Manager enables you to focus on creating a good plan to tackle whatever challenge(s) you're facing.

Here's what happened when I got my diagnosis:

—⁂—

May 24, 2013: Initial diagnosis and reaction (personal reflection)

I went to the ultrasound at an outpatient facility in the area. The exam seemed to take quite a while; the technician had a furrowed brow. Shortly afterward, a very worried-looking radiologist came in, asked a few questions about my symptoms, and then said, "Mr. Trice, we need you to get a CT scan this afternoon; we're concerned that there's something in your pancreas." Within 30 minutes I was getting the CT scan and after that was told that my general practitioner would call me. He called me on my way home, and gave me the tentative diagnosis.

He emphasized that they thought the tumor could be removed via the Whipple procedure, but because I'd already done some research on pancreatic cancer I had a good idea about how serious a diagnosis this was; even if you have a successful Whipple, your chances of living five years are only 20% or so, and half of those diagnosed across all stages die within a year. Still, I had to pull over to process the information for a few minutes.

When I got home, I immediately broke the news to Sharon and shared the dispiriting survival statistics. We held each other and cried; what else is there to do at that point in the process? Then, we pulled ourselves together and I prepared to make some calls to close family and explain the situation to our children (15 and almost 13 at the time). I tried to be as matter-of-fact about the whole thing as possible, realizing that I was going to need all of my strength and intellect to figure out a way through this cataclysm. I spent the rest of the long Memorial Day weekend doing more research about the disease, going out to a previously planned (and surreal) anniversary/birthday dinner with Sharon, making the family calls, and doing some initial contingency planning for how we'd handle the disruption of the treatments and deal with financial matters.

The Crisis Manager color role requires a combination of intensity and organization. Intensity is essential because of the high stakes and limited time. Also the Crisis Manager needs to impose some organization on the process to effectively set priorities and synchronize all of the activities and people involved.

Another key piece of this color role is contingency planning. Even as you are trying to come up with a plan for treatment or to meet another key need (e.g., covering regular household responsibilities), consider how different scenarios may require different resources or lead to different outcomes. What if the treatment you want requires traveling out of town? How would you deal with a particular side effect? What is the physical cost of waiting to see the specialist you want? Who will cover childcare while you're undergoing a rigorous course of chemotherapy?

In my case, one of the big things to be planned for was the treatment strategy—specifically where to get my surgery, and whether to participate in a clinical trial. I identified several institutions and surgeons with good reputations, visited them, and drew up a simple matrix with the pros and cons of each. Nothing too fancy, but a simple and effective tool to help me visualize the trade-offs I was making, discuss them with my wife and my analyst colleagues at work, and move forward with confidence that I wasn't missing something obvious. You can see the results of the planning in the message I rolled out to my support network:

June 6, 2013: Planning the work -- "Go Big, Go Long" (email)

All:

After the disheartening news on Tuesday [confirmation that I had cancer], we spent yesterday making some strategic choices about where to get the surgery and whether to participate in a clinical trial as well. Bottom line: we decided to have the Whipple procedure done at Hopkins, and I will also participate in a promising Phase II pancreatic cancer vaccine trial only available there. To get to this place required a lot of rapid information gathering, soul-searching, and consultation with some very smart and compassionate analyst colleagues at work.

Briefly, here are the layers of the strategy to get me better (not chronological). I call it the "Go Big, Go Long" strategy because it's the most aggressive alternative we studied.

Layer 1: The Whipple surgery at Hopkins; not optional. For this procedure, we are engaging Dr. Christopher Wolfgang, one of the two or three highest-volume performers of this surgery in the world; Chairman of the Pancreatic Surgery Department at Hopkins, and an intensive and long-time trainee under Dr. John Cameron, the father of the modern Whipple procedure. Also a Ph.D. in microbiology who understands the biological mechanisms of pancreatic cancer cells and can advise us on the best follow-on treatments.

Layer 2: The standard post-surgery chemotherapy and possibly radiotherapy treatment designed to prevent a recurrence. The details of this are to be decided later, and can be done locally in the Northern Virginia area.

Layer 3: The pancreatic cancer vaccine, designed to help the immune system attack the cancer of its own accord; it has shown promise in earlier studies, and we didn't feel the side effects or other risks were unacceptable. "Insurance on Insurance" is one way the study coordinator characterized it. There's a whole protocol here I'll spare you the details of, but the first dose is to be taken ASAP, with surgery to follow two weeks afterward.

Layer 4: The unparalleled support network of my family, clergy, friends, neighbors, colleagues, and survivors of this disease. This is as essential as any of the previous three layers, and wraps around them all. Every time I hear from you, receive your best wishes and prayers, get your email, consult with or vent to you, get to hang out with you, get some logistical or material help from you, I feel stronger and more optimistic--the feeling is palpable. I just can't thank you all enough for what you've done for me and my family already.

Sometimes the Crisis Manager must be called on in the midst of things, or if original plans don't work out. For example, a patient might unexpectedly develop acute problems under certain types of chemotherapy, requiring crisis management to resolve. For me, several weeks after my diagnosis, it took more crisis management to qualify me for the vaccine offered in a clinical trial. My liver panel numbers needed to come down to a particular point--by a specific date; when it appeared that the numbers weren't going to make it, I pressed the Hopkins folks for alternatives. The answer: send a bunch of IV fluids through my system in a hurry to flush out my liver. This procedure had to be done multiple times, and it took perseverance, focus, and tolerance of bladder discomfort to get me there, but I qualified for the trial, and believe my life has been extended because of it.

Increasingly, the medical profession recognizes that better crisis management and contingency planning can lead to improved patient outcomes (and conversely, unfortunately). A major UK study[9] acknowledged that cancer patients and their caregivers sometimes didn't know what to do when a serious physical problem occurred, and recommended that better patient and caregiver education about contingency plan-

9 Royal College of Physicians and Royal College of Radiologists, *Cancer Patients in Crisis: Responding to Urgent Needs; Report of a Working Party* (London: Royal College of Physicians, 2012), accessed October 22, 2015, https://www.rcplondon.ac.uk/sites/default/files/documents/cancer-patients-in-crisis-report.pdf.

ning be implemented. Good crisis management leads to good decisions that all of the key people agree on and give the patient the best prospects.

How You Staff the Crisis Manager

Experts in leadership and management[10] identify several traits effective crisis managers share, including being calm, authoritative, in command, considerate, constructive, and collaborative.

At this point in the cancer trek, can you stay calm, collaborate well with others, and prioritize and problem-solve well? If so, and if your physical symptoms don't get in the way too much, you are well positioned to be your own Crisis Manager—or at least the primary one.

If you don't feel up to being a Crisis Manager, either because you are overwhelmed or aren't sure you have the skill set, don't be afraid to ask for help. In fact, it's better to err on the side of asking for too much help than trying to do it all yourself, particularly in moments of crisis. It's not an all or nothing decision. You can reach out to others for Crisis Manager help if you want to vent and talk something out, if you need someone to take over another responsibility so you can focus on the crisis, or if you really do want help on the substance of the crisis.

Oftentimes the caregiver can step up to any of these supporting activities, if that's their personality and they're not too devastated themselves. Otherwise, seek out an organized and expert person in your support network, someone who might be willing to take on at part of the Crisis Manager color role or provide a sounding board for your decision making.

You also have the option of employing professional help. Nurse navigators, oncology social workers, and oncology nurses have expertise helping patients manage their emotions and assess their options; they'll also advocate for you within the medical and insurance systems and otherwise provide their specialized expertise experienced hand during the process.

---

10   See for example, Stan Toler, www.stantoler.com

Unless you happen to be an oncologist yourself, when the crisis is in the medical layer of the trek you must rely on the advice of your medical experts for at least some of the Crisis Manager color role. They have the knowledge and experience to interpret the situation and recommend different courses of action, giving you an objective basis on which to assess different treatments and their timing.

—∞—

Crisis Manager Color Role and Tint Interactions
Complementary color roles:

- Scout works well with Crisis Manager, depending on the time you have available, because Scout enables you to gather information, analyze it, and make better decisions.
- Publicist is also a useful color role to pair with Crisis Manager when you need to solicit help during the crisis.
- Crisis Manager probably will be used simultaneously with Patient and Warrior if you are in active treatment during the crisis.

Complementary tints: Crisis Manager is more effective when applied with

- Mindfulness: Maintaining a better emotional and spiritual state helps you calm the mind and make rational decisions.
- Optimism: Avoiding focusing too much and too early on worst-case scenarios enables you to direct your attention to the needs of the here and now.
- Proactivity: Being assertive about finding and seeing the best available medical experts.

Color roles that may conflict:

- Mortal: Reflecting on your mortality too much may encourage fatalism.
- Actor: Treating a crisis situation as normal risks living in denial and making things worse.
- Guru: Evaluating how you'd like to give back may not be the best use of time during a crisis.

—∞—

Crisis Manager Caregiver Connections
How to Help

Fulfill: Take over crisis management for the CC; become the focal point, the information hub, and the "calm in the storm." In extreme cases, you may even make treatment decisions if the CC isn't able to process the information or analyze the situation.

Partner: Act as co-pilot during the crisis by fully engaging in the information gathering and the decision making. You and the CC may work together or divide the tasks, but everything should be done by consensus with the CC.

Support: Provide logistical or similar services, like driving the CC to the doctor's office or taking notes at the appointment (often particularly useful if the CC is in a state of shock). Not all support need be direct; you might also pick up the slack in other household areas to give the CC space to manage the crisis.

Bystander: Choose bystander mode if you have a crisis of your own to manage, or if the CC's crisis has simply overwhelmed you. In either case, it's important to help delegate Crisis Manager duties to someone else.

Potential Conflicts

One partner may be in denial about the crisis. This typically occurs after the initial diagnosis or a similar medical crisis. The partner not in denial must help move the other forward so they can be effective as a team. Professional help from a counselor may be required to help the couple do this.

One partner may be indecisive. To prevent the time to make a decision from stretching out too much, the CC and caregiver can agree on a decision rule for moving forward—e.g., go with the most trusted doctor's recommendation, take the most aggressive approach, get just one more opinion and then make a decision.

The partners may disagree about the choice of treatment. When the caregivers has argued their case to no avail, it may be best to go with the CC's wishes. If the CC isn't committed to a particular course of action, it is less likely that it will be successful.

Mutual Support

Anticipate that meltdowns will occur, and permit them. Either when the crisis starts, or later, when the stress really gets to you, one or both of you will lose it. Whether it's a fit of rage, waves of sobbing, or some other strong expression of emotion, don't repress it, and hold onto each other when it happens. Wait until the emotions can be properly expressed before moving back into Crisis Manager.

Care for and be gentle with each other. Even if you are busy managing the crisis, watch out for each other. Both the CC and caregiver need to take breaks, eat properly, and try to sleep. If one partner stays in an over-agitated state for too long, seek professional help.

Understand how your skills complement each other's. If you had a good division of labor prior to the crisis, there's no reason for that to change. If you're good at organizing information, and the CC prefers schmoozing with strangers, take advantage of that. It's worth taking the time to inventory each other's skills and decide how you'd like to divide up the work.

Quick Wins for the Crisis Manager

If you only have five minutes: Send a text or email or make a quick phone call to help you address one small aspect of the current crisis. For example, you might set up an appointment, email a friend for help with a specific household need, or ask a medical professional a substantive question about your diagnosis or treatment.

If you only have fifteen minutes: Take a break from the stress and take a short walk, do mindfulness meditation, pray, or listen to music that calms you. The mindfulness tint discussed in Chapter 13 provides some suggestions.

If you only have an hour: Build or update your list of things that need to be done. Determine the order in which things can be done or what can delegated to others, then discuss your plan with your caregiver or other support person helping with the Crisis Manager color role.

What Good Crisis Managers Do

1. Take a breath, then prioritize
Let the shock of the diagnosis or change in prognosis sink in, then pull it together and decide what steps are most important for healing, recovery, or otherwise managing the current crisis.

A friend who took wilderness first aid told me that when someone gets injured out in the wild, the first thing to do is "smoke a cigarette."

This not a literal instruction, of course. The idea is do something that gives you a minute to reflect on the situation before making any plans—let alone acting--because if the injured party is going to die within the next few minutes, there isn't anything you can do about it right then anyway. Taking a few minutes for the shock to wear off allows time for a good plan to emerge.

A good plan in the context of a cancer-related crisis is one that reflects what's important to you. Maximum chance of a cure and a longer lifespan? Least amount of discomfort, fewer side effects, or less time spent disabled? Your doctors, counselors, and support network may give you good information about the different options and outcomes, but the CC needs to know their priorities before making the final call.

2. Break it down
When facing a daunting and overwhelming problem like cancer, you need a way to make the seemingly impossible doable or at least "startable". To do this, use the "chunking" technique: break down the complexity into bite-size pieces. List all of the small sub-issues, and start tackling them, either yourself or with help from your

support network. If a task isn't small enough to seem manageable, keep breaking it down until it's a something an ordinary layperson can do in a reasonable amount of time. You will build confidence pretty quickly if you can just get tasks down to the level where you can think about performing them.

3. If possible, take the time for second opinions

Seldom is the cancer so severe that you can't take a week or so to assess your options. Of course, if your condition requires palliative care or procedures to make you comfortable in the short term, that may be your first priority; but once that's settled, find the best surgeons and oncologists you can, and get their honest take on your situation. Early in the process, the time cost of gathering information may be less than the benefit it can give you.

4. Ask for help

If you don't enact the Crisis Manager color role at critical times, you run the risk of missing key treatment opportunities (due to, for example, insufficient research about the options or not meeting clinical trial criteria) or settling for an uninformed decision or even a bad outcome. Of course, focus and organization by themselves don't guarantee a good outcome, but a bad or overly emotional decision process certainly isn't going to help you. If you or your caregiver are unable to fulfill the Crisis Manager color role, seek help so you're not left to navigate the crisis without a guide. Don't let fear of asking for help hold you back; personal pride or embarrassment should be one of the first casualties of the crisis, so you can start getting the help you need.

In my own case, about a week after diagnosis I got into a bit of a funk, and needed support from friends to get me back on track as a Crisis Manager. Here's an email I wrote to a colleague who inquired about how I was doing. It illustrated that it's fine to ask for help for small things to enable you to work on the big things.

—∞∞∞—

May 30, 2013: Thanks for reaching out (email)

Thanks much for your concern buddy, coffee tomorrow would be great. I'm really on the edge here waiting for biopsy and figuring out what the surgery/ treatment is going to be. I have a couple of appointments with surgeons set up for next week now, so that's good to get the process going. But this thing is haunting me day and night.

What is the best course for maximizing my chances of survival? If things go poorly, how much time do I have left? What do I have to do to make sure my family is taken care of during this ordeal? Am I doing everything I can do to take care of them and myself? Managing work is a lay-up, but Major Illness Management seems beyond me right now.

Thanks for caring and noticing that I was a little off yesterday. We'll talk tomorrow. Thanks again.

5. Supplement your plan with subject matter experts

Cancer nurse navigators and specialized cancer clinics can help you see and plan out all of the aspects of your medical treatment that you've thought of, and some of those you haven't as well. They may also offer recommendations for other physical, mental, and alternative healthcare professionals. I was fortunate enough to have a vaccine research nurse at Hopkins and nurse navigator locally to assist me in seeing the whole treatment picture at different times in the process. Highly recommended.

You might also consider making early contact with fellow travelers; people who have the same kind of cancer and can relate their experience and wisdom to you. Right after my diagnosis, I spoke with several people who had experienced pancreatic cancer and/or the Whipple procedure—the side effects, complications, and recovery time expectations--and it was very valuable for my planning and decision making.

6. Build a project plan and contact list

Arrange your rides, your meals, and your appointments; as we'll see in the next chapter, there are online resources to make this easier. You may also prefer to ask others to plan out meals, communication, or child care for you.

Most importantly, have someone help you think through and integrate the issues you are facing. You may even want to convene your own "council of elders" to go over your options, but I wouldn't suggest totally outsourcing your treatment decisions--owning the course you take may improve your chances of success.

7. Don't second-guess your decisions too much

Easy to say, hard to do. It's always possible that another decision would been better in retrospect, but all you can do is make the best decisions possible under challenging circumstances, and move forward.

8. Limit Crisis Manager to short periods

It can't always be "4th down and 1" in football--or in life. We're not meant to stay in a state of hyper-vigilance. When the Crisis Manager color role is sustained for long periods, you risk grinding away at your mental and physical energies until you reach "shut-down" mode. You may end up planning poorly because you are working from a too-reactive posture.

Instead, reserve this color role for when it is really needed, like after a diagnosis or when urgent treatment--physical, mental, or spiritual--is required. When you're not in crisis, turn to other approaches that may require less focus and intensity. One such color role is the Publicist, which we'll discuss next.

— ✎ —

Further Reading on the Crisis Manager:

Michael G. Kavan, Thomas P. Guck, and Eugene J. Barone, "A Practical Guide to Crisis Management," *American Family Physician* 74, no. 7 (2006): 1159–64. Provides a family physician's perspective on dealing with the initial emotional impact of a serious disease; it's equally relevant to the patient and support group on the other side.

Royal College of Physicians and Royal College of Radiologists, *Cancer Patients in Crisis: Responding to Urgent Needs; Report of a Working Party* (London: Royal College of Physicians, 2012). Shows how contingency planning can help prevent crises in the first place.

Toni Bernay and Saar Porrath, *When It's Cancer: The 10 Essential Steps to Follow After Your Diagnosis* (New York: Rodale, 2006). Contains useful resources on navigating through the initial cancer crisis.

CHAPTER 5

The **Publicist** Color Role: Here's What You Need To Know

S cientists believe that chameleons change color to reflect their moods. By doing so, they send social signals to other chameleons.[11]

- Publicist **at a Glance**
  - *Key Transformation:* From being *closed* about sharing the realities of your cancer trek, to being *open* about the disease and the help you need
  - *Color:* Orange (think: enthusiasm and calling for attention)
  - *Description:* Communicate with others about your condition and needs: who, what, when, where
  - *Most applicable when:* you reach significant milestones, need help from your support network, or require an outlet for self-expression
  - *Strengths:* Updates your supporters and enables them to support you
  - *Risks of neglecting:* Isolation and inadequate help from your support network
  - *Risks of overdoing:* Too much information that overwhelms or distances you from others

How the Publicist Gives You Control

Unless you are living on Mars, when you get cancer you will find you have a wide and deep support network that will amaze and humble you. Family, friends, neighbors,

---

11 National Center for Families Learning, "Why Do Chameleons Change Their Colors?," *Wonderopolis*, accessed October 22, 2015, http://wonderopolis.org/wonder/why-do-chameleons-change-their-colors/.

work, clubs, and congregations, as well as potential new circles, like support groups, mental health professionals, and medical teams—together they form what I call the "deep bench" that is going to walk with you through the cancer jungle. "Deep bench" is a sports metaphor suggesting that several people can perform a given job competently (e.g., pinch hit, return a kickoff). The Publicist color role is what enables that network to come into being and sustains it.

The deep bench is there to help you, and that's great. But <u>you need to tell them how you're feeling and what you need</u>. This is true whether you decide you want to tap a bench of three or four people, or a bench of hundreds. The illness and its seriousness can cause people to feel awkward and uncertain about how to interact with and help someone and the diagnosis might shock them nearly as much as it shocked you. This may make them less inclined to approach you, which is why reaching out to them first and regularly can be so important. And finally, people are not mind-readers, so giving them some specific guidance makes them feel much more confident and helpful when they take steps to support you. And believe me, in all likelihood you are going need more help than you think at first, and it's worth going outside of your comfort zone to get it.

To tell them how you're doing and what you need, you must move from a closed mindset, in which you preserve your privacy and handle the cancer trek on your own, to a more open one. This is going to be pretty hard if your personality is introverted, you prefer to handle life's problems on your own, or you are emotionally overwhelmed. Only you can decide how open you want be and when to make that happen, but most CCs have to move some distance from where they start. And once you start reaching out, you will typically feel a greater sense of control about your situation as you feel the empathy and witness the offers of support that ensue.

What I think you'll find as you or a loved one enacts the Publicist color role is how many people care about you and the varied ways they will want to help you. Even when someone is unavailable to help you in a certain way, they'll offer a different kind of support; and another person will step up and do the first task for you. All of these experiences are quite empowering for the CC, because you will see that your team is more resilient than you might have first thought.

If you and your support team don't fulfill the Publicist color role, you may find that your care will suffer or you won't get the help you need. Worse, you may feel socially isolated. If you spent a lot of time away from your normal routines and social activities, it just reduces your contact with people, which in itself can just be depressing. I would advise you to take the trouble to be a Publicist even if it feels artificial at first; there will usually be a point in the cancer trek when you'll have a lot of needs, and you'll be glad that you stayed in touch.

Here's how some of my initial Publicist communications unfolded. I was biased towards communicating early and in some detail.

May 28, 2013: Quick update to family only (email)

All:

I'm sorry I can't call you all individually, but here is the additional data Sharon and I have about my condition after the visit with the specialist today:

1) The "abnormality" in my pancreas is at the head, measuring about 2.8cm by 2.6cm. That puts it into the "midsize" category, if you will. The good news is that from the CT scan at least, it does not appear to have invaded the major blood vessels running through the pancreas. The doctor will not have better fidelity on the tumor type until after tomorrow's testing, though the CT scan report states that "the head mass is highly suspicious for adenocarcinoma" (i.e. being cancerous). The biopsy and ultimately, the surgery will be more definitive about both the tumor and any extent to which it might have spread.

2) Tomorrow I will have an endoscopic ultrasound (EUS) with fine needle aspiration (FNA); in other words, they're going to stick a flexible tube down my throat and do a biopsy of the area. This procedure is done under general anesthesia and takes place in the afternoon; in the morning I need to do some blood work to validate that I don't have any bleeding problems or other abnormalities that would make the test unsafe. No work tomorrow, needless to say.

3) No matter what the findings of the biopsy are, both of my doctors so far have strongly urged me to undergo a surgery called the "Whipple

procedure" as soon as possible. Even if the mass is benign, it needs to be removed for proper functioning of my digestive system. This is a complex, major surgical operation best done by a place that does a high volume of these procedures; in this area specifically, Hopkins and Georgetown. My doctors are using their connections to get us a surgical consult and to be scheduled in for a procedure as soon as possible, assuming that I am still a good candidate for surgery as indicated by tomorrow's tests. Another reason to get the surgery done soon is that I am going to get jaundiced sooner or later, and if that happens before the surgery, it will cause further delays because they'll need to drain / "de-jaundice" me before I can get on the table.

I greatly appreciate everyone's support and prayers during the challenging days that lie ahead, and I will update you as soon as I have more information. Thanks.

A bit later on, I decided to provide a rather detailed accounting of my condition after some surgical consults. By this time, my support network had grown considerably to include just about all of my major circles, about one hundred people in all, and I had made the decision to communicate completely "open kimono"— not to hold anything back in terms of the severity of the diagnosis or my own state of mind. You may make different communication choices that are better for you.

June 4, 2013: Today's surgical consults -- "No rainbows and unicorns" (email)

All:

First of all, welcome to those new folks who have indicated they'd like to receive these updates. Conversely, if you'd prefer not to receive my updates for any reason, please let me know and I'll take you off the list--I won't be at all offended. I realize there is such a thing as TMI--this is just an efficient way for me to get the word out to a large group.

OK, so Sharon and I had extended and candid conversations with two very fine surgeons today ... and here are the unvarnished conclusions:

1) The mass I have in my pancreas is almost certainly cancer--they've both seen hundreds of images like mine and they'd both be shocked if the pathology tests came out benign or even just "pre-cancerous". In my last message, I warned about getting too excited about the biopsy results, and this has been borne out. Apparently, even a malignant tumor only has 10-15% of its mass populated with what a layperson would call cancer cells, so the fact that the biopsy didn't find them was unremarkable.

2) We are probably looking at a Stage II cancer, like I said in a previous note, a "mid-sized" tumor that may or may not have spread to local lymph nodes, but with no evidence of distant metastasis. So this gives us a fighting chance long-term, but we are looking at chemo and/or radiotherapy at some point after I recover from the surgery.

3) The good news is they both confirmed that I am a viable surgical candidate to get this thing resected via the Whipple procedure (tumor not spread to key surrounding veins and arteries), so we are still moving full speed ahead on that front--I only need to pick my surgeon and whether I am going to participate in a clinical trial at Hopkins involving a "vaccine" (basically immunotherapy to attempt to train the body to fight cancer cells on its own).

I think one of the surgeons set the mood for us today -- "I talk to people about cancer all the time, and there are people who talk about it in terms of rainbows and unicorns, but I'm not that guy." I need the professionals giving me the facts, I've had my allotted five minutes of feeling sorry for myself and am trying to stay strong and focused, and I gather my strength and focus through your support and prayers. I'll be staying home tomorrow to deliberate about my best course of action, and make that choice by Thursday so we can get this show on the road.

Thanks again.

--Andy

The Publicist color role is most useful when you have reached a significant milestone or when you need to communicate a need for support. It's also good for routine updates because your family, friends, and acquaintances are always worrying about you and wondering how you're doing. Sometimes you may need to teach people a little bit about the nature of your condition as well as give status on it.

How You Staff The Publicist

Publicist may not be one of the jobs you asked for when you got cancer, but it's one you've got on top of everything else. A very wise rabbi once told his congregation that the four most powerful words in the language may be "I need your help." So reach out and ask for it—and do your best to get past any shock, shame, embarrassment, or reluctance holding you back. Publicist has to be staffed at some level, even if you don't like the idea.

As with any color role, how to staff the Publicist depends on your capabilities, inclinations, and energy level. For some people, communicating (especially by writing) can be a valuable form of self-expression and healing in its own right--as you might guess, that's the case for me or I wouldn't be writing this book. If you're like that, you might be a good CC Publicist; but if you have many of those attributes, but feel shy, you can start by describing the facts of your situation; you don't have to write wide-ranging essays or get dramatic or mushy. If it was your friend who had cancer, what you would want to know about their situation? People will appreciate whatever you put out there.

Not everyone likes to write or orate, whether sick or well, and that's ok. Dividing up the Publicist responsibilities (by the mode of communication or people communicated with, for example) is one alternative. You can also engage a trusted member of your support network to communicate for you if you don't feel like it, don't feel comfortable communicating, or it seems like a burden. Choose someone close, like your caregiver or a good friend who knows you well. If that's the case, be aware that unless you can vet the material that goes out first, you may "lose control of the message," typically in the sense of more being shared than you are comfortable with. Letting the person know what your preferences are may mitigate this issue.

Publicist Color Role and Tint Interactions
Complementary color roles:

- Crisis Manager works well with Publicist, because as a Crisis Manager you need to communicate with many people to get the help you need.
- Patient is supported by Publicist, to the extent you solicit help for the logistical aspects of treatment (e.g., transportation to appointments or meals or visits while convalescing).

Complementary tints: Publicist is more effective when applied with

- Humor: Keeping communication light and interesting will make your messaging more enjoyable and get positive responses from your support network.
- Proactivity: Being assertive about asking for what you need makes it easier for others to help you.
- Relationships: Communicating with people with whom you are on good terms makes it easier to be candid and straightforward.

Color roles that may conflict: It's important for the tone you convey at any given time to matches up to any other color role you're emphasizing.

- Mortal: Isn't a fit for Publicist if you're feeling optimistic.
- Warrior: Isn't a fit for Publicist if you're working through tough symptoms and side effects and you feel more like acting than talking.

Publicist Caregiver Connections
How to Help

Fulfill: Be the primary communicator of the CC's condition and needs; make all the choices about what to communicate and to whom. This works well when the CC just can't bring themselves to share anything, but permits you keep the support network informed, at least to a degree.

Partner: Divide the Publicist work with the CC, whether by contributing material to publicize or vetting potential communications with the CC before sharing it with others, or sharing responsibilities for getting messages to different audiences.

Support: Act as "ghostwriter" and conduit for the CC, like by consulting with them or helping the CC brainstorm a list of needs or of people who need to be informed of new developments. You may also edit the material the CC or others write, post it online, or make calls for the CC at their behest.

Bystander: Choose bystander mode if you don't have the energy to act as Publicist, or truly don't believe that publicizing the CC's needs will save you time or stress in the bigger picture. In fact, you may choose instead to confide in a small number of people about the stresses you are facing as a caregiver.

Potential Conflicts

One partner may not want to share information they view as too private. This could be anything from physical condition to feelings to the prognosis. Obviously this situation implies a negotiation process between CC and caregiver to determine what will ultimately be shared. One way to tackle this is to segment the audiences, sharing more personal things only with family or selected close friends.

One partner may not want to reveal the extent of their needs to each other, let alone to the world. This could happen when one partner doesn't want to "burden" the other, or feels ashamed of the situation. When this occurs, private counseling may be in order so the two parties can figure out how to broach the need with each other before moving on to broader audiences.

Mutual Support

Take advantage of your differences. If one of you loves to share while the other is private, the sharer can be the Publicist (assuming there are no other conflicts). If one partner feels more comfortable with friends and the other with family, or each has their preferred method of communication (telephone vs. social media, for example), parcel out the Publicist work accordingly.

Ensure your partner is in the loop and ask for permission prior to communicating particularly sensitive information. During my own trek, there have been a couple of times that I communicated things about the seriousness of my diagnosis and prognosis (based on research I had done) and blasted it out to my entire distribution list before informing my wife. Bad idea. She had valid concerns about both having a chance to process the information herself and about the children inadvertently getting this news from others rather than from us.

Enable the caregiver to get help too. For CCs with caregivers who are spouses or partners, please note that getting help from your broader support network is also a way to keep your loved one(s) on an even keel. No one person can ever fulfill all the needs of another; there's no reason to expect this to be any different when you get sick. Your caregiver is probably just as overwhelmed as you, so if you don't want to ask for help for your own sake, ask for it on their behalf. Even in the absence of a serious illness situation, no one person can ever fulfill all the needs of another; why should we expect this to be any different when we get sick?

Quick Wins For the Publicist

If you only have five minutes: Draft a quick update paragraph on how you (or the CC, if another person is playing the color role) is doing, and save it for later review.

If you only have fifteen minutes: Contact a family member or friend to give them a more detailed update on how you're doing, or to vent.

If you only have an hour: Rethink your "strategic communication plan" (see the four W's described below) so that it fits your current needs. For example, if you have been sending out weekly updates but treatments are at a lull, you may need or want a break. Alternatively, perhaps there is an untapped audience that you'd like to reach out to (e.g., a congregation or club).

What Good Publicists Do

1. Choose your four Ws: who, what, when, and where
There's no one right set of choices here! Just make sure you tailor your plan to suit your needs and temperament. The book listed in Further Reading at the end of this chapter provides some communications checklists you may find useful.

Who to communicate with: Who do you think cares about your condition, and how much privacy do you desire? Your answer may change over time: at first you may feel too overwhelmed to share much but may open up more as you grow accustomed to the situation and can identify your needs. You may also want to stratify your audiences into close family, friends and supporters, etc., and share different things with those audiences as your trek unfolds.

What to communicate: How much detail do you want to provide-- just medical information, requests for support, more expansive essays, or some combination? The answer will depend on your energy level, talents, and personal preferences or privacy concerns.

When to communicate: Do you want to do this regularly, when the need or desire arises, or at significant milestones only?

Where to communicate: Do you feel more comfortable pushing out emails , talking one-on-one over the phone or in person, setting up a website with or without alerts, or using social media (e.g. Facebook, or Twitter)?

Don't discount the structured electronic tools for communicating and organizing support (e.g., CaringBridge[12] or LotsaHelpingHands[13]). These sites make it easier to distribute information, enforce your privacy, and enable people to sign up to help.

---

12 www.CaringBridge.com

13 www.LotsaHelpingHands.com

2. More is usually better than less, particularly when using media people can digest at their own pace

A Publicist's work can be overdone, to be sure. You can be undisciplined in your communications, either by not "allowing yourself the luxury of an unexpressed thought,"[14] giving information that is too clinical or overly detailed, or coming across as too self-focused. But for most people, more communication is better than less.

When I began my blog, I was shocked by how much people appreciated and enjoyed the commentary, and no one ever complained (as far as I know) about information overload. I think the fact that email and web content are things that people can read on their own time had something to do with that; if I had ranted at length in person when someone needed to get to their next meeting, I would certainly have understood had they become impatient with me.

3. Tune the message and media to your own personality, need for privacy, and need for support

What is true in life in general is true here: there is no substitute for being yourself. If you are genuine in your approach to communication, people will respond to you; if it seems forced, it will fall flat. And recognize that while people may be concerned about how you are doing, they will respect your privacy if you don't want to disclose your feelings or certain details of your physical condition. In this situation, perhaps you simply share more personal information with people closer to you.

4. Don't get too cute or complex; make the message accessible

This is pretty basic too. You can't assume people have a scientific background, and they don't want to have to wade through layers of literary symbolism to get your message. I wrote one post that drew an analogy between my situation and a baseball box score. I think a few people got it, but overall it went over like a lead balloon. People were like, "I got your latest post, man. What happened?" (Mercifully, I chose not to include that post here)

14　A statement attributed to the late Sen. Everett Dirksen, as told to Sen. Howard Baker of Tennessee, and a favorite family quote.

Sometimes, simply distilling essential information is the most important service you can provide. This early blog entry gave those who had just found out about my condition the essential facts about my condition, written in an easy-to-read FAQ-style format:

———⬡———

Welcome, and FAQs about Andy's condition

posted by Andrew Trice, Monday, July 1, 2013

Thanks for visiting our site, which we will use both for communicating salient developments in my medical situation and matching people in the community with tasks on which we can use some help.

Since there's so many new folks signing on to the site now (thank you!) I thought I would provide some baseline information for everyone's reference in case not everyone's up to speed.

Q: When did we find out I had a pancreatic mass (almost certainly cancer)?

A: Late May, right around our anniversary and my birthday. Pretty evil, huh?

Q: What is the operation I'm having?

A: The Whipple procedure, to remove as much of the tumor that's in the head of my pancreas as possible and reconnect what remains to the rest of my digestive system. Complicated abdominal surgery--average is six hours.

Q: How long will the hospital stay and convalescence be?

A: Average hospital stay--seven to ten days, possibly longer with complications (about 40% of patients). Convalescence is typically a few weeks. Patient is usually weak and has trouble keeping weight up for quite some time.

Q: Is it acceptable to make jokes about passing gas being my ticket out of the hospital?

A: Of course.

Q: Will there be other treatments later, like chemo or radiation?

A: Yes. In my case, I've already received an experimental pancreatic cancer vaccine only available at Johns Hopkins, and will continue to receive dosages approximately monthly for a year as long as I continue to qualify. I will also have chemotherapy and possibly radiation--all depends on the pathology report and how aggressive we go on the treatment. This is a marathon, not a sprint.

Q: What has the response from and support of the communities around Andy and Sharon been like?

A: Absolutely unbelievable.

Q: What is working in my favor, given that I have this dangerous type of cancer?

A: See the last question. Also, I am relatively young to get this disease, am in good physical shape, my symptoms have been relatively mild, and indications are the tumor has been caught early enough to be resectable (removable).

I hope this is information is helpful. Stay tuned. Thanks.

--Andy

---

5. Don't risk alienating others by telling them what you don't want; tell them what you do want or appreciate

People mean well even if they're not perfectly articulate or haven't gamed out the second- or third-order implications of their statements or actions. It's best to tell your support network what you appreciate and slough off anything that misses the mark; if you focus on telling people what you don't want, they might be more tentative in approaching you.

In this chapter we've seen how effective communication can help you gain control through informing and energizing your support network. Though the Publicist color role and the communication mechanisms we've covered here are critical, sometimes your communication is bound up in how you behave on an everyday basis. This, as we'll see in the next chapter, brings in the Actor color role.

Further Reading on the Publicist:

Toni Bernay and Saar Porrath, *When It's Cancer: The 10 Essential Steps to Follow After Your Diagnosis* (New York: Rodale, 2006). A book chock full of communication strategies for cancer patients; includes several useful worksheets for Publicists.

CHAPTER 6

The Actor Color Role: Cancer? What Cancer?

W hen these lizards are in calm relaxation mode, they usually simply blend in with the rest of their environment, in true inconspicuous chameleon style. If you can barely detect the presence of a veiled chameleon, there's a good chance he's taking it easy.[15]

- Actor **at a Glance**
    - *Key Transformation:* from feeling *marginalized* from mainstream life and social activities, to *engaging* with the outside world in meaningful and authentic ways
    - *Color:* Yellow (think: joy, happiness, and hope)
    - *Description:* Go about your everyday activities as if you had no illness; reclaim or rediscover a sense of self
    - *Most applicable when:* you are between treatments, in remission or stable, or when you're managing appearance changes
    - *Strengths:* Help you improve mental and physical health by going out in the world and doing regular things
    - *Risks of neglecting:* "Sick person" stigma; everyday tasks neglected, leading to a disordered, stressful everyday life
    - *Risks of overdoing:* Denial, poor self-care, inability to focus on the bigger picture

---

15 Milburn, "Identifying a Veiled Chameleon's Color and Mood."

How the Actor Gives You Control

No matter how much of your attention cancer takes up, it is never the totality of your identity. Focusing on a dread disease and its implications all the time will make you crazy; you were a unique person before cancer, and you'll continue to be unique during and after your cancer trek.

One good way to enact that uniqueness is to act like the disease isn't there. This not as counterintuitive as it might seem; as you go through your cancer trek, you will probably find that the cancer is not all-consuming all of the time. In fact, you may be surprised how quickly the "new normal" can feel like the "old normal," and that's a good thing.

The Actor is about evincing normalcy to those around you by acting as you would if you were disease-free. It is a particular face that you convince yourself is authentic and show to the world. It enables you to preserve—or rediscover—your identity, and to prove to yourself that you can do it. This has some important implications.

Actor affirms that you are more than a person with a disease. Once you get cancer, people may be more interested in you, but they won't necessarily assume you are a "regular person" anymore. They will take their cues from how you look, how you talk to them, and how (and whether) you reference your cancer. If you act "normal," they're going to be more comfortable treating you normally too, even though they may have lots of questions and concerns about your condition. But if you don't have the Actor color role in your toolkit, you risk feeling like just a "sick person," and like it or not, in most societies that carries a certain stigma.

The Actor color role is most often applicable when you are between treatments (provided you feel well enough), and during periods of remission or stability. But it can also be employed for shorter periods when you just need a break from the intense focus on your illness. It also provides a distraction from the rigors of a treatment program, and from your aches and pains. studies show that people who are more socially engaged tend to have better health, no matter what their age or condition[16].

---

16 See, for example, Debra Umberson and Jennifer Karas Montez, "Social Relationships and Health: A Flashpoint For Health Policy," *Journal of Health and Social Behavior* 51, no. S1 (2010): S54-S66; for cancer in particular, see Adelaida Zabalegui, Esther Cabrera, Montserrat Navarro, and María Isabel Cebria, "Perceived Social Support and Coping Strategies in Advanced Cancer Patients," *Journal of Research in Nursing*

One of the key outcomes of the Actor color role is discovering the joys of getting back to normal. When I was recovering from the Whipple surgery, it was great to re-engage with life a little bit and get out. I ate like crazy to try to gain weight back, went into work briefly, and even felt well enough to go out to a restaurant with friends for the first time in a month.

Back Online and Going Mainstream!
posted by Andrew Trice, Wednesday, August 7, 2013
Hello all:

So I hope no one was concerned that it's been more than a week since the last email. I'm pleased to report that in the last several days there have been a number of encouraging signs and events.

First, it appears I'm finally turning the corner on the weight gain -- up several pounds from my nadir that stubbornly held for at least a couple of weeks. Partly it's a digestive enzyme medication adjustment, partly it's that I've begun to figure out what foods disagree with me, and partly it's just brute force slamming five meals a day into my system. For your amusement, here's a typical day in the Andy anti-emaciation diet:

6AM: big bowl of cereal, whole milk, and a big pastry, with an dark chocolate Ensure chaser.

9AM: some sort of heavy egg and cheese thing (e.g., strada, quiche, bacon/egg/cheese biscuit)

12PM: cheeseburger and fries, or a Mediterranean mezah, or some other robust lunch

3PM: protein shake or milkshake with added whey protein, ice cream, maybe a banana

6PM: whatever Sharon cooks up, maybe spaghetti carbonara, or cheese grits, or pork tacos slathered with cheese and sour cream...

Looking at this now, it kind of has the feel of a slightly sophisticated Homer Simpson diet, only without the Duff beer. Anyway, it seems to be starting to work and is in alignment with the considered advice of my registered dietitian, so who am I to quibble? Plus, it's the only thing about my condition that people seem to be envious of--the opportunity to eat irresponsibly and not feel guilty.

Second, as a corollary to item one, the Four Horsemen of the Digestive Apocalypse (bloating, belching, cramps, and diarrhea) are rapidly receding, which, in addition to being more comfortable overall, has significantly improved my sleep. My system is figuring out how to make the new wiring work, just as the experts and fellow travelers kept telling me.

Third, my energy level is steadily improving. I had the pleasure of going into work for a visit yesterday, and my colleagues and I were struck by the delta between my stamina at work two weeks prior and yesterday. After two and half hours, I was feeling like I wanted to stay and work, rather than being exhausted. The earlier time, after an hour and a half I was pretty exhausted and needed to be given a ride home.

This is all adding up to making me feel almost "normal" (ok, normal except needing to take some breaks to rest during the day and avoiding heavy lifting). Last night, Sharon and I went out to eat with friends for the first time since my surgery. It was so great to be able to eat a good dinner, sit around comfortably and converse with friends, and generally be out and about. I even shared a BEER with Sharon, to no ill effect.

My only concession to the illness was to get up periodically and walk around to aid my digestion and relieve the pressure on my (unpadded) backbone and posterior. But as I was doing so, I was marveling at the whole thing--one month ago, ICU and a gutted digestive system; today, walking around pain-free and eating in a restaurant, feeling mainstream rather than marginalized (not that I've ever really felt marginalized, due to the support and contact you have all provided every step of the way, but I think you get my drift).

So yes, I'm pleased with my progress right now if you can't tell. I've also decided to go back to work part-time beginning on August 19th, with the schedule to be flexible based on the exact schedule of my follow-on treatment and my reaction to it, thanks to my fantastic and accommodating management team at work. In the meantime, I continue to try and gain weight and strengthen myself for the third inning of this game, later in the month: more vaccine, chemo and radiotherapy.

Let's go get 'em. Thanks.

Finally you may also choose to play the Actor color role in managing the changes in appearance cancer often brings. This is an area in which individual differences are particularly broad. For example, faced with hair loss due to chemotherapy, a CC may wear hairpieces, headscarves or hats; proactively cut hair very short before it falls out; go openly or defiantly bald; or a combination of these. In the end, it's much less important what you choose to do about your appearance (or for that matter, any other behaviors) than that you do so authentically and in the way that helps you best heal and relate to others.

How You Staff the Actor

Unlike many of the other color roles, Actor can't be delegated; everyone else is in a supporting stance, though caregivers and the larger support network also have to define their own Actors in terms of their relationship with the CC. Examine your capabilities and inclinations, understand what the new normal is for you, and then engage with others on that basis.

Actor Color Role and Tint Interactions

Complementary color roles:

- Philosopher helps support Actor very effectively, because it gives the CC a larger perspective on what's really important (e.g., completing a bucket list or working on family or career milestones vs. tasks that could be outsourced or aren't a priority).
- Publicist helps support Actor, because you can use your communication skills to engage with others on non-medical as well as medical issues.
- Guru helps support Actor, because if Guru helps the CC to understand what sorts of "pay forward" activities are most meaningful, then this can guide the Actor's everyday activities.

Complementary tints: Actor is more effective when applied with

- Passion: Savoring every day with enthusiasm enables the Actor to be more productive and enjoy time with others more.

- Optimism: Anticipating the return to future normal activities even if they are limited now gives you the hope to keep going and improve your capabilities later.
- Relationships: Enjoying life as fully as possible through interactions with those who are important to you will enrich your time enacting Actor all the more.

Color roles that may conflict:

- Crisis Manager: Doesn't work well with Actor because it crowds out the time available for any kind of normal life.
- Mortal: Looks so far forward and focuses on things not being okay, it's hard to play that in conjunction with Actor.
- Warrior: Is so focused on toughing things out that Actor is probably better reserved for other times.

Actor Caregiver Connections
How to Help

Fulfill: While you cannot play Actor for the CC, you can be your own Actor – in the sense of maintaining slices of normalcy in your own life, and a sense of yourself as an individual. In fact, being a good Actor can often help the CC play the color role better themselves, because it gives the CC tacit permission to play Actor also!

Partner: Help cultivate a sense of normalcy and authenticity by doing the things you enjoyed doing together before the diagnosis--insofar as that's still possible.

Support: Facilitate the things the CC wants to do while playing Actor; transport them to special events, help them make adaptations so they can get to work, or encourage the CC's friends and family to find ways to connect. Supporting everyday activities like going for a cup of coffee, attending leisure activities, or speaking about any topic other than cancer are all good too.

And don't be afraid to reach out and initiate non-medical interactions and activities. It can mean a lot to the CC when you solicit advice from them in an area where they have expertise, or otherwise treat them as a regular friend or colleague.

Bystander: You can choose be a bystander by simply letting the CC pursue their own outside interests, particularly if they seem motivated or eager to do so. The idea is to tacitly support the CC's enactment of Actor by giving them some independence, so it's key to avoid undue fussing –even if you have worries about whether they are up to the challenge.

Potential Conflicts

One partner may be more emotionally attached to the cancer than the other. This could arise when one partner feels like their life is so defined by the cancer that it's difficult to access any kind of normalcy, while the other would like to be able to move past making cancer the focus, at least in certain aspects. As long as the partners can be mutually respectful of their differences and allow each other to be Actors to the extent they feel comfortable, this is not a problem. But if there is resentment (e.g., the CC feels abandoned because the caregiver is doing something fun on their own), frank communication or professional counseling may be in order.

One partner may be in unhealthy denial about the cancer, and use Actor as a way to deflect discussion of serious issues. Sometimes it's healthy to behave as if the cancer isn't there. But what if one partner always tries to pretend that it doesn't exist, even if the prognosis is extremely serious or the CC is obviously unwell? This is the opposite of being too emotionally involved; the Actor has gone too far. The partner in denial may need to be lovingly confronted, again perhaps with some professional help.

Mutual Support

Use a spectrum of stances towards one another. To play the Actor well, it pays to be conscious of the different ways you can do that relative to your partner. I believe that in a healthy marriage you need to spend some time face-to-face (working explicitly on your relationship), some time walking in the same direction (working on shared enterprises like child rearing, or home improvement), and some time walking in opposite directions (pursuing your own separate careers, interests, and relationships). These stances can all be applied while enacting Actor.

Work on your relationship: A cancer trek generates strong emotions, and discussing these openly helps you navigate the new normal of your relationship. Often the rigors of the trek and its accompanying fears will make the partners realize how much they need each other and how much the survivor would miss the CC if the cancer turns out to be terminal. In this sense, the CC and caregiver may deepen or restructure their communication patterns, allowing their time as Actors to be more meaningful.

Move forward together: Evaluate how the cancer trek will affect your previous division of labor, and plan your Actor color roles accordingly. Any permanent physical changes in the CC may mean the caregiver has to pick up the slack or delegate some responsibility to a third party. Or perhaps the opposite has occurred; the CC has developed new skills or wants to step up to do more while the cancer is in remission.

Give each other permission to do some activities separately: Even though time with one another may seem more precious than it did prior to the cancer trek, both partners are whole persons who are more than the relationship, just as they are not completely defined by the reality of the cancer. Personal authenticity requires striking the balance between togetherness and separateness, even if the balance looks a little different now.

Quick Wins For the Actor

If you only have five minutes: Take a mental break from the rigors of the trek to indulge a guilty pleasure of some sort.

If you only have fifteen minutes: Plan a whole day of diversions that have nothing whatever to do with cancer.

If you only have an hour: Talk with your partner about how the cancer trek has affected one or more of the three "stances" mentioned above.

What Good Actors Do

1. Keep as much of your regular routine as is comfortable for you, plus special activities that are meaningful to you
Cup of coffee in the morning? Walking the dog? Hanging out at work? Figure out which of your previous routines felt good to you, and stick to those if your health permits. You'll be surprised how much these activities will energize you and make you feel like your time was well spent.

2. Limit discussion of your illness
If people ask how you are doing, feel free to tell them, but don't let them dwell on the subject. Bring them up to date briefly and accept their best wishes--then, ask them how they are doing too. This will put them at ease and make both of you realize you are more than your cancer. Sometimes you may find yourself mixing Publicist and Actor together; give people the update, then go on to other topics of interest.

3. Bracket and fence off your cancer -- wait to worry
A major point of the Actor color role is to get you out of your cycle of worry about the disease. Believe me, you are not going to heal yourself by sheer force of worry, so try to clear those thoughts away—at least for a while.

4. Prioritize doing things that help others
Life continually presents us with all kinds of non-cancer problems that need to be addressed, and you or someone else has to pick up the slack.

When you are in treatment and others are helping you cope or otherwise uplifting you, anything you can do in return for them counts as a victory. I never thought I would get so much pleasure from taking out the trash until I couldn't do it for a while because of limitations on how much the doctors allowed me to lift. You learn to appreciate the seemingly mundane tasks, because you remember what it was like to not be able to do them.

5. "Fake it to make it", within limits

Even if you're not feeling great, try to engage with others in the outside world, whether it's in person, on the phone, or electronically. As the 12-step folks say, sometimes it's worth using a "fake it to make it" strategy; People will invariably respond to your energy and give you more energy in return, creating an encouraging, positive exchange between you. At the same time, you can't be an Actor all the time--cancer is going to intrude, sometimes in a major way. In the extreme, the Actor denies the reality of the illness and prevents you from taking proper care of yourself or looking after the strategic management of your disease. If you're feeling really crappy, "fake it to make it" isn't going to cut it, and the people around you should understand that. The Actor needs appropriate balance just like all the other color roles.

—⚬⚬⚬—

If you act the part of a well person whenever you can, the world will respond in kind. But conserve your strength; there will also be plenty of occasions when it's time to toughen up and become a Warrior.

Further Reading on the Actor:

Be the person you were before cancer--or better--as much as you can. There's no resource for that other than you.

CHAPTER 7

The **Warrior** Color Role: Bring It On and Dig Deep

*C*hameleons will also use bold color changes to communicate. Males become bright to signal their dominance and turn dark in aggressive encounters.[17]

- **Warrior at a Glance**
    - *Key Transformation:* from feeling *intimidated* by the cancer and its threat to health or life, to *fighting* actively against the disease
    - *Color:* **Brown** (endurance and reliability)
    - *Description:* Fight the cancer with courage, tenacity, and integrity; bear pain, trials, and indignity with strength and hope, even during crisis
    - *Most applicable when:* working through intense treatment and rehabilitation
    - *Strengths:* Brings resolve, persistence, and attitude to the fight; may extend lifespan
    - *Risks of neglecting:* Failing to fully engage in the healing process when resolve and determination is required
    - *Risks of overdoing:* Exhaustion from staying in "fight" mode

How the Warrior Gives You Control

The term "cancer warrior" is in danger of becoming a cliché, but it still has great power. The word "warrior" connotes a certain strength, courage, and sacrifice that embodies those who serve a noble cause. For you as a CC, the cause can be as simple as your

---

17 Bates, "How Do Chameleons Change Colors?"

own survival, as deep as your desire to be there for your family, or as broad as a mission to serve humanity. It will provide you with the drive that enables you to move from being intimidated by the cancer to fighting actively against it, thus achieving control through defiance and determination.

Warrior is most effective when you face surgery, pain, treatments, side effects, and other challenging experiences. Immediately after my surgery, with stitches the length of my middle and multiple tubes running out of me, being a Warrior was about my only option. I was still in a drug-altered state when I wrote this short note, but I wanted my support network to know that I'd taken the first step towards healing--by getting through the massive operation and waking up. Thank God for pain medication.

I'm doing well

posted by Andrew Trice, Thursday, July 4, 2013

It's Andy. Moved into regular room today, pain under control, good spirits. Just stood up for first time too!

A couple of weeks later, I had returned home but was suffering from the usual bumps in the road expected from major abdominal surgery that rejiggers the whole digestive system. It's no accident that I used a sports metaphor to describe how I was feeling at the time. At moments like this, you need to enact the Warrior frame of mind to get through it.

Nothing like Delayed Gastric Emptying to give you perspective

posted by Andrew Trice, Thursday, July 18, 2013

Hello all:

Thinking of sports metaphors today. As I pass the Surgery+15 day mark from the Whipple, it's becoming clear to me that I've moved from the phase of this recovery game where rapid gains can be made to the phase where you measure progress in inches, one small meal at a time. It's all changed from those heady days where by sheer spirit and willpower, you can work harder and heal/get active faster.

It's not a football game of exciting plays and gaining noticeable field position; it's the world's slowest golf game, where every day is a like one hole and every meal is a shot you take, then you see where the wind and course conditions take your shot. Sometimes the shot settles nicely, moving towards the green (yay! digestion successful!); sometimes, it goes into the rough (Ugh! this hurts, but it'll eventually go down), and sometimes, it goes into the gallery and the fans reject you entirely (use your imagination).

What's going on? A phenomenon known as "Delayed Gastric Emptying (DGE)." Simply put, in DGE your new, smaller, shocked stomach isn't (yet) doing a good job of moving your food through to the small intestines in a timely fashion via the pulsing actions it normally does, resulting in a backup of food and fluids. You may have pain, bloating, nausea, or worse while this is going on. It's something all Whipple patients experience to some degree for some time, though only 20% of patients have it so bad that intervention is required and it's formally called a "complication." Talking to Hopkins today and telling them my symptoms the last three days, they said "Dude, sorry, but you're well in the range of Whipple normal here. Be patient and kind with yourself."

I wonder if this whole experience is some sort of spiritual marathon where there will be ten or so big events, each of which test part of your character in a different way. We're just in the patience/nausea tolerance event now. The event will be over when eating is more comfortable, my weight stabilizes and starts moving back up; just not there yet.

In the meantime, thanks as always for your contacts, visits, and all the rest. I'm ok, just still in the belly of this particular beast (get it)?

If you don't bring your Warrior to the fight, you risk giving only half-hearted energy to the healing process. In my times at hospitals and other treatment centers, I have observed wide variations in the Warrior energy different patients appear to have. It's not for me to judge how much anyone should enact Warrior at any particular time; indeed, there are times when you just can't be a Warrior, or even shouldn't be, like at end-of-life or when rest is the first priority. But there is an observable difference between the energy level of someone enacting the Warrior and someone who isn't, and someone with a fighting spirit will tend to have more resilience and staying power on the cancer trek.

There are countless examples of cancer warriors in literature and popular culture. One celebrity who epitomized the Warrior archetype is ESPN announcer Stuart Scott. Scott fought metastatic cancer of the appendix for eight years, enduring numerous surgeries, recurrences, and rounds of chemotherapy. Nonetheless, he said, "I can't ever give up" because he stated that "I can't leave my daughters" (Scott was a single parent). Scott continued to work and exercise vigorously--even while doing his treatments--until the very end. While accepting the Jimmy V Perseverance Award on national television, he said that you do not lose to cancer when you die, but rather "you beat cancer by how you live, why you live, and the manner in which you live."

These are inspiring words for all of us with cancer, and words that exemplify the Warrior ethic. Don't give up. Live for others. Work through the pain, tiredness, vomiting, and other physical or emotional setbacks. You can--and should--enact the Warrior as long as you have something to live for. The Warrior brings resolve and persistence to the fight, either extending your effective lifespan, increasing your energy, or at least giving you the satisfaction that you are doing your best. My slogan for the Warrior is "Bring It On and Dig Deep"; it conveys a willingness and even eagerness to take on whatever the cancer dishes out, coupled with the psychological strength to keep relentlessly pushing on.

How You Staff the Warrior

Like the Actor, the Warrior color role is one the CC really has to own to enact. A serious illness is as much a test of character as it is a physical challenge; you need to decide what you are fighting for and how hard to fight for it. But this must remain within reason; your ability to enact Warrior depends on how long and how seriously you've been sick.

Warrior Color Role and Tint Interactions

Complementary color roles:

- Patient helps support Warrior, because by following recommendations on medications, rehab, and other medical instructions, you'll be better positioned to make it through challenging times.

- Actor also works well with Warrior; showing a normal outward posture makes it less likely that you will be pitied, allowing you to focus more on recovery and get positive energy from others.
- Crisis Manager supports Warrior, to the extent that effective crisis management enables you to focus on getting through treatment rather than taking up too much time managing emergencies.

Complementary tints: Warrior is more effective when performed with

- Humor: Lightening up a pretty harsh situation helps everyone involve cope better.
- Optimism: Anticipating a future with less discomfort gives you extra strength to carry on.
- Forgiveness: Exercising self-forgiveness especially enables you to stop beating yourself up after a setback and move on to the next challenge.
- Mindfulness: Using this as a tool for changing your perspective, and as a pain management technique, can be valuable.

Color roles that may conflict:

- Mortal: Doesn't combine well with Warrior because mortality is what the Warrior is acknowledging yet fighting against.
- Guru: Isn't very active while you're in Warrior mode, because of Warrior's intense focus on the present moment rather than on long-term issues.
- Philosopher: Same rationale as with Guru.

—⊶⊷—

Warrior Caregiver Connections
How to Help

Fulfill: Unless the CC has an out-of-body experience and inserts your body, you can't fulfill Warrior. Full stop.

Partner: Act as the Warrior's companion during the pain, not in the sense of taking it on yourself (impossible) or merely making sympathetic noises, but by being truly present during the CC's toughest moments. This means different things to different CCs; for some it may be physical contact for comfort; for others, distraction from pain; for still others quiet confidence or encouragement at a workout or treatment session.

Support: Be present during the struggles, encourage the CC, and otherwise create the conditions that allow them to focus on and excel in the fight. This could include driving them to treatment or physical therapy sessions, providing inspirational materials, or ensuring the CC is taking pain or other medications to avoid unnecessary discomfort or side effects. You can also support the CC by picking up the slack in other areas-- household or family needs--to allow the CC to focus full-time on their fight.

Bystander: Choose bystander mode by allowing others to be the Warrior's companion or supporter. Many caregivers find watching their beloved Warrior in action to be emotionally difficult and a major cause of burnout; you aren't the only one positioned to help your partner with Warrior, so don't feel guilty about letting others share the load sometimes.

Potential Conflicts

The caregiver wants the CC to be a "stronger" Warrior. This is tantamount to the caregiver wanting to fulfill the Warrior when they just can't. The manner in which Warrior is enacted is a deeply personal choice; there is a fine line between encouraging the CC and encroaching on their autonomy. When in doubt, err on the side of letting the CC define what a good Warrior is for them. In fact, trying to "make" the CC be a Warrior, or suggesting it's an obligation to themselves or others, may just as likely backfire as motivate.

The CC insists on playing the Warrior alone. This is the opposite problem—the CC thinks being tough means refusing to accept the help they need and that the caregiver desperately wants to provide. In this case, it's appropriate for the caregiver to remind the CC of the difference between the smart Warrior who, like a good soldier, knows that the mission is bigger than any one person, and the misguided Warrior, who thinks heroes act alone.

Mutual Support

Talk about the Warrior color role explicitly. When contemplating treatment options or in the midst of a rigorous treatment course, a frank conversation about how much pain and physical or mental challenge the CC is willing or able to take on is very useful. It will help you both clarify decisions and cause less resentment down the line.

Quick Wins For the Warrior

If you only have five minutes: Read a short excerpt of material that inspires you or gives you perspective on how you can keep moving forward in spite of the difficulties you face.

If you only have fifteen minutes: Do your favorite mindfulness practice to help you deal with any present discomfort.

If you only have an hour: Research an upcoming treatment (surgery, chemo, radiation, clinical trial) to better understand the side effects or potential complications and think about how you might mitigate them.

What Good Warriors Do

1. *Find your inspiration*
There are innumerable books and blogs about cancer Warriors, providing a wide range of perspectives on the topic. Some use martial arts metaphors; others are straight personal memoirs that focus on religious faith as inspiration, or integrate alternative and complementary medicine approaches into the mix.

These authors talk about the various places they find their strength to fight (e.g., family or other loved ones, God, a higher purpose, a particular life philosophy, or sheer willpower). There's no one way to play Warrior; however, I encourage you to go through some of these materials to try to find your own source of strength. The references at the end of this chapter provide a sampling of what's available.

2. Look ahead to prepare your mind

Being prepared for a challenging experience, even if you are frightened about it, can empower you by giving you information that gives you a sense of what you could be facing. Preparing could include individual study, consultation with medical professionals or laypeople who have gone through a similar treatment (as described in the Crisis Manager chapter), or a formal class. For instance, you can take classes about chemotherapy prior to taking the plunge, where they talk about the experience, the side effects, and the potential complications.

It's not that different from first-time parents taking childbirth classes – you want to know what you might be in for, even if you can't fully appreciate the event until it happens. Then you can use this information to prepare yourself mentally for many of the possible scenarios--including what can go wrong. In my case, I was so prepared for the Whipple to be an arduous (or even life-threatening) experience that when I did better than the average patient, with manageable pain, I was ecstatic.

3. More action, less talk

Warriors set an example through how they behave, not so much how they talk about it (blog posts notwithstanding, granted). When you work hard at healing and getting stronger, people will notice and help you stay positive. If you complain every time you have discomfort or are frustrated with your progress, you're going to be tough to be around—and that may make it less attractive to others to support you, despite the extensive of amount of sympathy and admiration they may have for you.

4. Work through mental as well as physical pain

It's easy to think about a Warrior toughing it out through physical pain, but sometimes the mental pain of cancer is every bit as bad. If you suffer bouts of loneliness, depression, even despair, know that it's a common issue many Warriors face. Cancer throws you off the routines you cherish in the short term, and even more ominously, raises the specter of there not being a long-term for you. However, there are treatments and other, informal ways to help deal with this mental pain. Informal chats with supporters, mindfulness techniques, professional counseling, or appropriate medication all can provide critical mental and emotional support so you can be a better Warrior and fulfill other color roles as well.

5. Exercise to expand your capabilities
Because exercise is about keeping in shape physically and spiritually within whatever constraints you're facing, one popular component of the Warrior color role is physical exercise. How this plays out will vary greatly from person to person depending on pre-cancer condition, personal temperament, and phase of treatment and recovery; but whether it's just getting up to walk around, or training for that next triathlon, Warriors push themselves to get in the best shape they can. Exercise requires discipline of thought and action, both key to the Warrior ethic.

6. Set "stretch" goals for your physical progress
Arnold Schwarzenegger once said that no conditioning program gets very far without specific goals. I found this to be true too. Until I put a marker down to say, do that 5K run on a specific date, or get back to lifting the same amounts in the weight room as before, I didn't have anything to work towards. Do the same yourself, even if you think your goals are relatively modest. If it's motivating to plan a reward for reaching the goal, so much the better.

7. Don't be a martyr; manage all of the side effects you can
Warriors aren't successful based on the amount of pain they can bear; their job is to bring all available tools to bear to fight the cancer. And this involves dealing not only with the underlying illness, but the side effects of its treatment. In fact, medication, when used wisely, may make you a better Warrior because it can extend your capabilities and resilience; the world of pain relief can be a wonderful place, and everyone who can should take medication in appropriate doses to give them relief so they can concentrate on recovery or everyday activities rather than their pain. To do anything else when you have the option is, not to put too fine a point on it, stupid. Those who

develop tolerance to pain medicine or have unacceptable side effects to it are a different class of Warrior altogether and have my admiration and sympathy.

8. Understand the different modes of medicine for cancer, and what they mean relative to the Warrior

The type of medical support and the way you enact Warrior go hand in hand, and understanding that enables you to fine-tune your approach to it.

First, there are medical measures with *curative intent*, that is, you're trying to make the cancer go away forever. Many Warriors will put up with quite a bit of pain or great inconvenience (e.g., major abdominal surgery, physical isolation, extensive travel), because of the potential payoff.

Second, there is treatment to *manage* the disease and *extend life*, but not cure the cancer. Many chemotherapy regimens are like this; they work for a time but may not destroy all of the cancer in your system, leaving you vulnerable to a future recurrence. While a Warrior may opt for this type of treatment as well, the trade-off feels different from the curative intent measures. For instance, are you willing to endure a reduced quality of life for many months to extend your lifespan for just a few months?

Third, there is *palliative care*, which used to connote end-of-life treatments to make a patient feel more comfortable, but is now acknowledged as synergistic with the other two categories as well. The Warrior should <u>always</u> strongly consider appropriate palliative care, even if primarily undergoing curative and management treatment. Anyone who doesn't is simply going through needless suffering. Caregivers, please emphasize this point to your CC! Pain management is not just for end-of-life situations anymore. Less pain means more capacity to fight.

9. Push, but don't injure yourself

No one has ever reached higher levels of conditioning without pushing themselves to some degree, and recovering from cancer treatments is no different. That said, if you're injuring yourself by overdoing it or eating only to vomit your food right back up, you may need to be more gentle with yourself. Sometimes healing has its own pace, which takes some emotional strength to accept.

Being a Warrior can have its downside too. For one thing, it's exhausting. You can't be on patrol all the time; even Medal of Honor winners need some downtime. And sometimes the best thing you can do to get better is simply to rest and let your body's normal healing processes do the work, which is what being a Patient is about.

Further Reading on the Warrior:

Nate Miyaki, *The Way of the Cancer Warrior: 34 Strategies for Your Cancer War* (Nate Miyaki LLC, 2014, accessed October 22, 2015, http://natemiyaki.com/wp-content/uploads/2014/09/Way_of_the_Cancer_Warrior.pdf. Thirty-four principles drawn from the martial arts tradition. Plenty of unremitting inspiration and fighting spirit to be found here.

Alana Somerville, *Chemosabe Cancer Warrior* (Alana Somerville, 2012). A teacher's experience of self-empowerment and advocacy. Particularly useful for breast cancer.

Toni Bernay and Saar Porrath, *When It's Cancer: The 10 Essential Steps to Follow After Your Diagnosis* (New York: Rodale, 2006). The chapter on managing side effects of treatment is particularly insightful.

Ruth Levine, *Cancer Warrior: Where the Mind Goes* (Minneapolis: Quill House, 2011). A memoir that includes useful meditation and prayer techniques to aid the Warrior; the author takes a Jewish perspective.

Vivian Mabuni, *Warrior in Pink: A Story of Cancer, Community, and the God Who Comforts* (Grand Rapids, MI: Discovery House, 2014). A faith-based approach to the Warrior; the author takes a Christian perspective.

Christine Horner, *Waking the Warrior Goddess: Dr. Christine Horner's Program to Protect Against and Fight Breast Cancer* (Laguna Beach, CA: Basic Health, 2013). Integrates alternative and complementary medicine approaches with the Warrior role.

CHAPTER 8

The **Patient** Color Role: Get With The Program

A chameleon that is drab is generally stressed by something in its environment, sick, or too cold. [18]

- **Patient at a Glance**
  - *Key Transformation:* from being *wounded* by the cancer or its attendant treatments, to participating in the *healing* process, physically or emotionally
  - *Color:* **Green** (think: healing)
  - *Description:* Undergo and comply with medical procedures, treatment protocols, and side effects; engage in self- and nursing care
  - *Most applicable when:* undergoing surgery or treatments, whether in a facility or at home; and when taking medication throughout the cancer trek
  - *Strengths:* Helps you heal more quickly, or reduce pain
  - *Risks of neglecting:* More pain and poorer outcomes
  - *Risks of overdoing:* Self-victimization, depression and anxiety

How the Patient Gives You Control

Here's the dreary truth: to deal with most types of cancer, you are going to spend significant time in doctor's offices, treatment centers, and hospitals, and there will be

---

18 Petra Speiss, "The Vieled Chameleon (Chameleo calyptratus) Purchase and Captive Care," Kingsnake. com, accessed October 22, 2015, http://kingsnake.com/rockymountain/RMHPPages/RMHveiled.htm.

plenty more time during recovery when you just feel weak or otherwise not up to par. Sometimes the process will be fraught with emotion and high drama; often you will experience some discomfort; and always, there's a measure of schlepping, waiting, and boredom.

Welcome to the world of the Patient; the world of going through the hoops, following what the medical experts say, enduring the tedium and healing time, and otherwise doing what it takes to get better. Many patients also integrate additional wellness or complementary treatments into their regime, which can greatly aid the healing process, but are also time-consuming and interact with conventional treatments.

Whatever the specifics of your treatment and recovery, the goal is to move from feeling or being wounded to engaging with the healing process. I had to engage with this healing process after my major operation. When it's going well you can sense the healing momentum accelerating, and it's a great feeling.

On the Road Again
posted by Andrew Trice, Friday, July 5, 2013
Feeling great today [two days after the Whipple] as we ease back into actually ingesting some calories. I won't lie--last couple of days were very hard work--but it felt really good to do some more serious floor lap work today and stretch my legs, powered by apple juice, broth, and Jell-O. I can feel all of the major muscle groups loosening up and it feels good to be able to sit upright in a chair and enjoy some normal society with family and friends up here as opposed to being essentially bedridden.

Overall, the sensation of a Whipple procedure for me was as if someone smushed all of your internal organs together and tied knots around them. I found it most helpful to practice deep breathing (to the point of some discomfort) and some quasi-yoga movements (sun salutation-type stuff) to avoid slipping into the "hunched shoulders curled up into a ball" posture because your stomach hurts so damned much. Thanks H!

Feeling the Power

posted by Andrew Trice, Saturday, July 6, 2013, 5:45 PM

Had the first chance to talk with the surgeon late yesterday afternoon. He said the tumor they removed was larger than the 2-3 cm reported from the CT scans--4 cm. But that's not bad, because it was due to the inflammation caused by the vaccine attacking the tumor. Also, they only had to excise about 25% of the pancreas, leaving plenty of organ for normal functioning over time.

The real goal of the vaccine is that it will also attack any cancer in the hidden places where it may crop up later. He characterized the surgery Wednesday as "the first step on the road to cure." We'll take it!

The past four days have been very physically painful, but also extremely powerful. To feel and hear the support of all of you during the healing process has been like nothing I've ever experienced. I can measure my progress every day, and we appear to be on track for making it home next week some time, barring any significant complications.

Breakthrough Day

posted by Andrew Trice, Monday, July 8, 2013

OK, on day six at Hopkins we see the progress accelerating.

At 6:00 AM rounds, docs said I was ready for some more substantial rations, even though I had not (yet) performed the bodily function that dare not speak its name.

By 9:00 AM, off IV meds and fluids entirely, and ordering breakfast. Walking around without tubes and IV poles is awesome.

By 10:00 AM, slowly chowing down on eggs, cereal, and toast. Funny feelings in tummy, did I overdo it? Stop and wait.

By 11:00 AM, realize food really is taking, no nausea.

By 11:15 AM, blubbering with happiness like a Bizarro-world baby. Just for eating regular food successfully? Really?

Also ate some lunch later (soup and pudding). Worst time was around 2 p.m., when I realized I had gone from significant IV pain meds yesterday to NOTHING today. Collapse in recliner! Malaise, debilitation, and fever! How could I be so stupid? All is lost. Get me some OxyContin stat! Sharon very concerned. Take medicine and wait. By 3:30 storm clouds have passed, feel just fine again.

The next, and perhaps final, gate to the finish of the inpatient segment of this race is a lab test done tonight to see if there are any leakages coming from my pancreas. Should have results tomorrow on this.

Yay.

—∞∞∞—

Home
posted by Andrew Trice, Tuesday, July 9, 2013
Mission Success. Resting comfortably in living room recliner provided by mother-in-law. Nothing more invasive to be found on me than a band-aid. Tired but gratified. With the help and encouragement of all of you, we have checked the first big box on the list of things needed to get me better.

Thanks so much to everyone who played a part in making this possible.

—∞∞∞—

The Patient color role is most applicable when you're going through the medical procedures themselves. But you will need to be a Patient outside the hospital, like when you do chemotherapy or radiotherapy on an outpatient basis or even while you continue treatments at home. In this context, you are something in between a Patient and an Actor, as illustrated by the following post:

—∞∞∞—

The Land of the Zapped Centaurs
posted by Andrew Trice, Saturday, September 21, 2013
I'm feeling good after the first three radiation treatments. No side effects (yet; there will be some transient tiredness and possibly digestive stuff later); still doing all normal activities like exercise and work. Here's a brief inside look at my radiation oncology crib (imagine teenage daughters cringing as I just said that):

You stroll in, and as you walk around the hall you see about six imposing looking machines from behind thick doors, each of which has an evocative high-tech name ("Synergy," "CyberKnife," "Thor") and signs like "Beam On" next to them. The patients sit in little waiting rooms, one per machine, and look! They can't decide whether they are sick people or people off the street! From the waist up, institutional hospital gown; from the waist down, street clothes. It's like they're some new variety of mythological figure; modern-day centaurs perhaps.

As you go into one of the rooms with a machine, you see the patient lying down on a table in a completely vulnerable posture, with abdomen exposed and hands above the head; it's like a diagram out of the dog obedience school "submission" lesson plan. As the patient lies there, various large plates and laser beams rotate around them. They start, they stop, they vibrate, they make "Star Wars" noises. We assume the machines know what they are doing and won't beam the patient into a black hole or something.

But in the end, it's all painless and after a few minutes, the patient is done. See you tomorrow! (Unless it's the last treatment, in which case you get to ring a special bell they stole from Trader Joe's.)

It's a profoundly dichotomous experience really. You look kind of sick; you look kind of well. You are totally vulnerable on the table; you are benefiting from the most powerful high-tech physics weapons medical science has to offer. The treatment is completely invisible; yet the treatment has effects deep inside your body at the cellular level. The machines emit powerful radiation such that no one else can be in the room with you; but the whole point of this is make you well by zapping the cancer. But all in all, I'm very grateful that we're going straight for the original target at this stage.

Enjoy the rest of your weekend.

How You Staff the Patient

Since it's your body we're talking about, there's no way around it; only you can fulfill the Patient color role. As with Warrior, the help your family and friends provide is primarily in the support mode.

I think most of us know what kind of Patient we are. There are "good" Patients who naturally do what the doctors prescribe, and there are those who need more support—difficulty remembering to take medication, physical limitations, or even attitudinal issues (e.g., skepticism about treatments). There are Patients who want a lot of TLC, and others who prefer to keep their reliance on others to a minimum. Either way, the staffing has to be driven by the temperament of the CC.

Patient Color Role and Tint Interactions
Complementary color roles:

- Warrior goes hand in hand with Patient, because a CC who has a strong will does whatever it takes to get better, including following medication recommendations and otherwise taking care of themselves. In fact, Warrior time periods tend to overlap heavily with Patient time periods, with a caveat: a poor Patient may have more need of Warrior, because they may not heal as fast.
- Publicist can make for a better Patient experience, because the emotional support and practical help you get through communication enables you to be encouraged and focus more on the healing process.

Complementary tints: The Patient color role is more effective when performed with

- Proactivity: Keeping medical professionals informed of any difficulties you're having will your care and the set of possible medical solutions.
- Optimism: Anticipating a future with less discomfort and more capability helps your morale, just as with Warrior.
- Relationships: Engaging with others staves off boredom and self-pity over a potentially long period.
- Passion: Keeping the momentum and dedication to your self-care going may improve your results.
- Mindfulness: Using this as a tool for changing your perspective and for pain management can have substantial benefits, as in the context of Warrior.

Color roles that may conflict:

- Mortal, Guru, and Philosopher: None of these combine well with Patient, unless you are the rare CC who takes comfort in thinking through longer-term issues while you wait to heal, and you have the temperament to not be overwhelmed by weighty thoughts.

Patient Caregiver Connections
How to Help

Fulfill: As with Warrior, since it's the CC's body, it's the CC's job to fulfill Patient, not yours.

Partner: Be the CC's advocate with medical and psychological professionals if the CC isn't up to it or can't make direct contact with them. Since you are likely the one most in tune with whatever the CC is experiencing, you may be in the best position to offer this level of support. I can tell you from experience that this can be absolutely huge for the CC who is ailing; my wife made a few interventions for me when I was in the hospital that I didn't have the good sense to see I needed.

Support: Support the CC Patient by doing whatever you'd do if your partner had a less severe illness like a flu or bad cold. This could include reminding them to take their medicine, adjusting physical accommodations like beds or pillows, preparing or bringing food, helping with the Patient's mobility, or creating other conditions for healing that are more environmental in nature (e.g., ventilation, light, pleasant surroundings). Of course, if the CC is in a hospital or other comprehensive facility you will be a supplement to the professionals rather than the primary supporter (and if not, you need to find another facility). But even so, there are many non-medical ways you can support the CC, such as providing simple companionship, or other distractions like reading material or games.

Bystander: Hire an assistant caregiver to cover some of the tasks noted above. Whether you are just not a natural nurse or healer or you need some respite care, don't feel ashamed about choosing bystander mode and getting help; while it's understandable to want to be the heavy lifter here, you can't overdo it. Your life's purpose cannot be limited to being caregiver for the CC.

Potential Conflicts

The caregiver and CC do not agree about the treatment or the medical professionals they like. This is akin to the situation where a couple tries to be friends with another couple, and someone just doesn't click with the others. Communication is key here; get the issue on the table and try to work it out. Maybe you'll uncover facts or impressions that will reconcile matters, or one of the partners will decide to accommodate something they view as second-best. If the discrepancy can't be resolved the caregiver may need to move towards a bystander mode, and the let the CC make the final call.

The caregiver feels like a nag, or the CC perceives the caregiver as a nag. When the stakes are a lot higher than taking out the trash, small things like one too many reminders about medicine could set a normally calm person off. The only prescription is to be gentle with each other and avoid making assumptions about what the other has done or not done.

Mutual Support

Watch carefully for signs of depression in each other. When you experience discomfort for longer than just a few hours, the world tends to look bleaker to both the CC and the caregiver. This book is not a mental health primer, but it's safe to say that if one of you is constantly crying or apathetic for long periods, I strongly suggest getting some outside help.

Understand that having patience works both ways. One of the hardest parts of the cancer trek is accepting that there will be periods when one or both of you can't do normal activities, even basic ones. And it's not just because of the CC's physical limits; the physical and emotional burden on the caregiver makes it tough for them to focus on everyday activities also. It's understandable to feel angry that things aren't "normal" for a while. Openly acknowledge your feelings with your partner and only then try to get beyond it.

Quick Wins For the Patient

If you only have five minutes: Reflect on any discomfort you might be having in the moment and come up with a few ways to address it.

If you only have fifteen minutes: Make a realistic list of activities you'll do once you feel well enough.

If you only have an hour: While you're at an appointment or in residence for your treatment, focus on being as pleasant and solicitous as possible with everyone you meet.

What Good Patients Do:

1. *Do what your doctors say*
This is pretty basic. Move where they tell you to move; exercise when they tell you to; take your pills and other meds as prescribed. You've chosen your medical professionals and the treatment course, and now you need to give it a chance to work. This is what being a Patient is about.

This doesn't mean that you shouldn't ask questions if something seems off to you; but the Patient has to be, well, patient with the dynamics of the healing process. There's a time and a place for researching the future, but right now your job is to heal.

2. *Be persistent with the logistics of your care*
Being a good Patient doesn't end when you leave a treatment facility. Keep following to your medical professionals' instructions, even when they can't check up on you. It's

a startling fact that many Patients don't do this once they are outside of the hospital. A recent study indicated that married people with cancer did better than single people, perhaps because the spouse helped the patient remember to take their meds.

Planning and scheduling is one way to ensure you're following the doctor's orders; it's easy to forget something when you're sick or in recovery. When I had all of my prescriptions together or knew the schedule for the day I felt a sense of order and control independent of whatever chaos was going on in my body. Even if you're not a planning type, you may benefit from this kind of organization (or have someone do it for you). Management tools make it simpler; pill packets, mobile apps, alarms, and more.

3. Empathize with medical staff and caregivers

If you were a harried doctor, nurse, or aide, who would you be more likely to take a little extra time with--a nice Patient or a grumpy one? Swap jobs for a minute and consider what kind of day the medical worker is having. Sometimes being a good Patient is as simple as saying, "Thanks for taking care of me." Just smiling (even if you don't feel like it) may be beneficial too, and trying to be pleasant to someone who's in a bad mood gives you extra points.

And don't forget about that unpaid (and possibly cutting back paid hours elsewhere) person in your home who's doing the heavy lifting. A little appreciation for caregivers like spouses or other relatives will go a long way.

4. Customize your self-care to meet your needs

My hospital room, which I called my "healing hut," was a place of calm, simplicity, lack of clutter, music, and yoga practice. But everyone has their own needs and preferences. Whether you like having photographs or art to look at; prefer to integrate complementary medicine or bodywork into your routines, or want to spend time praying or meditating within your faith tradition, figure out what self-care means to you, and go for it with passion.

Self-care goes beyond environment or mindfulness, too. Part of being a Patient is dealing with a lot of downtime. When I got lonesome or bored during the long days in the hospital, I tried to find something enjoyable and productive to do, like writing or calling others, but you may prefer other activities, such as entertainment distractions. Having visitors, if you're up to it, is a particularly encouraging way to break up the monotony.

5. Slow Down

As a Patient, the only person you're competing against is yourself—and the competition is to see how well you can remember it's not a contest. The best way to succeed at Patient is to go about the business of healing and self-care and not set artificial deadlines.

---

posted by Andrew Trice, Tuesday, September 10, 2013
Friends,

Things continue to move in the right direction. Energy getting better all the time, played tennis and hosted some guests over the weekend, approaching pre-surgery jogging pace (working on endurance), back to lifting weights (albeit at lower levels than before, given the muscle mass loss). Someone even told me I was looking "infinitely better" today compared to a few weeks back, which made me wonder if I looked like death warmed over before, but I think it was just some well-intentioned hyperbole. Finally, my weight is still seeking "escape velocity," i.e. it's still going up, just very slowly at this point. I'm hoping the exercise will actually facilitate some muscle-building, with an accompanying increase in weight. But overall, I'm focusing more on how I feel than hitting a specific number.

---

6. Accept where you are, but keep evolving to get better

Having a resilient attitude is another important part of being a good Patient, because the trek isn't always smooth. You can't expect that recovery will be a straight line up; there will almost always be complications, side effects of treatments, reactions to medications, and other setbacks. It may be two steps forward, one step back; or even one step forward, two steps back for a while.

If you are feeling down, it may be helpful to get a different perspective from someone else. I have several friends who play the part of "anti-devil's advocate" for me; that is, when I tell them about a concerning diagnosis, symptom, or statistic, they remind me about the other side of the issue. My daughter did a good job of this for me one time during my radiation treatment:

Is there a specification for resilience?
posted by Andrew Trice, Sunday, September 29, 2013, 2:00 PM
After the good progress of the last several weeks, it feels like the recovery machine has hit some mud, or at least a bump. The last few days, I haven't been able to sustain the energy and activity level I had through the first week of radiation therapy. Over the weekend, I've needed to conserve energy and cut back on my workouts. I'm just kind of tired, and my digestion isn't feeling quite right. Takes its toll. Sharon says I've been trying to do too much and need to take it easy; I reluctantly agree. Most insulting of all, I'm down a couple of pounds from the recent post-surgery peak.

But in the words of the old Civil Rights song, I've got to "Keep my Eyes on the Prize" and "Hold On, Hold On." The real prize isn't to set cancer patient athletic records or maintain an ideal weight; it's to get better. Julia (fifteen year old daughter) provided me with a good perspective on this today, as evidenced by the following exchange:

Julia: So, you're kind of tired now.
Me: (Sigh) Yeah.
Julia: That must mean the radiation is working.

And understand that in today's cancer treatment landscape, there is often a whole range of treatments available, and if one isn't sufficient, another one may work better. Don't give up hope if one treatment doesn't do the trick. Another option may be even better. Conversely, if the healing process is going well, report it—and keep the momentum of healing going.

Being a Patient requires you to be dependent, at least for a time. This is very hard to do for many people.

It is also important to know when to shift away from being a Patient. When you re-cover from surgeries and treatments and become more mobile, find another color role to focus on instead. If you stay in Patient mode when you don't have to, you may begin to view yourself as a victim of your fate,[19] leading to a greater risk of depression and anxiety.

When you're ready to move past being a Patient, you'll want to start thinking more about the future--and that is what the Scout in the next chapter is all about.

Further Reading on the Patient:

Jonathan Chamberlain, *The Cancer Survivor's Bible* (Brighton, UK: Long Island Press, 2012). Chock full of guidance on the cancer trek, including the wide range of medical experiences possible.

Jimmie C. Holland, *The Human Side of Cancer: Living With Hope, Coping With Uncertainty* (New York: HarperCollins, 2001). A physician writes about what she's learned from her own patients.

---

19 See, for example, Crystal L. Park, Ianita Zlateva, and Thomas O. Blank, "Self-Identity After Cancer: "Survivor", "Victim", "Patient", and "Person With Cancer," *Journal of General Internal Medicine* 24, no. S2 (2009), S430-S435.

CHAPTER 9

The **Scout** Color Role: What's Next?

Perhaps the strangest of animal eyes belong to the chameleon. They are mounted in twin conical turrets and can move independently of each other, giving the chameleon the ability to see all round itself when seeking prey, and binocular vision in front when it is preparing to strike with its long, sticky tongue.[20]

- **Scout at a Glance**
    - *Key Transformation:* from *trudging* through the cancer trek one difficult step at a time, to *navigating* diagnosis, treatment, and recovery by evaluating different courses of action
    - *Color:* **Purple** (think: vision)
    - *Description:* Identify what may lie ahead and gather information about your treatment options
    - *Most applicable when:* towards the end of specific treatment phases, or during downtimes
    - *Strengths:* Enables more options and better mental preparation for future developments
    - *Risks of neglecting:* Uniformed decisions and strategic surprise (being blindsided by a difficult treatment or prognosis)
    - *Risks of overdoing:* Obsession to the point of inaction, too much potentially dispiriting information too soon, clashes with medical personnel

---

20   Allie Miller, "Eyes Give 360 degree Vision: Chameleon," Ask Nature, Accessed October 22, 2015, http://www.asknature.org/strategy/f6b73865a35b39d2974e29905e8b1a8c#.VHx6zRAhC1k

How the Scout Gives You Control

A Scout reports about what lies on the horizon, possibly over a wide angle of vision like our chameleon friends. It can be a dispiriting job if they look out and discover an enemy that possesses overwhelming force. But the information can empower the commander of the army to plan the battle more effectively, because they will better understand what they are facing and what their own order of battle should be.

Scout is the color role that enables you (or your support network on your behalf) to be proactive about the treatment of your disease. The research and planning you do may generate new options for your treatment, make the treatments go more smoothly, and in conjunction with Publicist, get you better assistance from your support network. There is also an intangible psychological benefit; Scout activities prepare you mentally for the different paths the illness can take. And doing any planning at all is preferable to simply trudging through your cancer trek, putting one foot in front of the other but feeling no sense of control over where you're going.

Perhaps the most extreme example of a Scout is Ralph Steinman, a Nobel Laureate in Medicine from Rockefeller University who was diagnosed with pancreatic cancer in 2007. Realizing how intractable the disease could be, he designed his own clinical trial of one by custom-producing his own cancer vaccine;[21] he not only looked ahead, but invented his future. Now, not everyone has the skills or knowledge to attempt such a forward-leaning cure for themselves, but all of us can take some responsibility for thinking about what lies ahead.

Here was my first foray into the Scout domain, when I had confirmed my treatment strategy and received a surgery date:

———✖———

---

21 See Daniel Engber, "Is the Cure for Cancer inside You?," *New York Times*, December 21, 2012, http://www.nytimes.com/2012/12/23/magazine/is-the-cure-for-cancer-inside-you.html. Sadly, Steinman died four years after diagnosis and three days before winning the Nobel, but the immunotherapy he applied to himself might have lengthened his life.

June 10, 2013: Working the Plan -- Closing In (email)

Hello all:

Today, I went to Hopkins again (thanks to brother Jeff for the ride and companionship), met with the vaccine trial coordinator, signed the consent forms, and got another liver function blood test to assess whether I could start the vaccine today. The good news was that all of the numbers are improving significantly--the stent is doing its job well. The (only slightly) bad news is that only two of the three numbers have gotten below the threshold needed to give me the go-ahead, and on this test, you need to bat 1.000. So we wait until next Monday to start (provided the third number makes it down by then); and I can get the other blood tests this week done locally.

All that said, it was very worthwhile to go up because I learned more about the vaccine trial and what to expect if/when I do start, and, most significantly, learned that the surgeon's scheduler has put us down for the Whipple surgery on Wednesday, July 3rd. It turns out that his schedule has been rejiggered and there were some very pressing patients to be worked in, so this was going to be the date we ended up with in any case. So it's simple now: numbers come down by end of this week, start vaccine next Monday; if not, I won't do the vaccine at all. Surgery will happen July 3rd in any case.

With this date in hand, we can now begin to make some more concrete plans and start slotting in our magnificent array of people who have offered to help out into specific roles/dates/times. Thanks, and stay tuned.

OK, so the tumor has been put on notice that its days are numbered, and my network of agents may start working on it and its pesky little sleeper cells even sooner. I don't know why it appeared (either biologically or existentially), but it sure has gotten me a lot of attention and love and discomfort and gut-wrenching angst. Now, a new era is closing in; an era with a lot more trials and a lot less cancer inside me. Thanks, more than I can ever express, for holding us up while we navigate into it.

Andy

---⧟---

Scout is the color role you enact when you can afford to think past "one day at a time"--when you want to understand more about your disease so you can game out other options and map out treatment schedules and logistics. In short, be the Scout when you, as the commander of your own army, want to understand, and then apply, what's next.

If you don't enact Scout, you may have to scramble to arrange for treatments or make uninformed decisions that give you poorer outcomes. You may also find yourself blindsided by new developments or side effects if you haven't done your research in advance; it's best to avoid this sort of "strategic surprise," which requires extra adjustments to overcome.

---⧟---

How You Staff the Scout

It takes a particular type of person to enact the Scout, and if you're not into it or can't face it, there is plenty of space here for others to help out. Good Scouts have intellectual curiosity, analytical ability, and the capacity to be objective. You have to be motivated to search out alternative treatments, talk with different doctors, look at scientific data in peer-reviewed journals, and critically evaluate different treatments in terms of success rates and side effects.

For the CC, the capacity to be objective is perhaps the most challenging. If you feel like you've got your hands full fighting for your life, you might not want to dwell on data that tells you your chances are slim. (I've learned to chuckle at the almost universal opening to research papers on pancreatic cancer, usually some variation on "Pancreatic cancer has dismal survival statistics...", but your mileage may vary.) But if you're motivated and able to separate the statistics from your own individual situation and realize that anyone has the potential to be an individual case rather than a statistic, you as a CC may be well-suited for the job.

If not, anyone who has the Scout's traits can fulfill the capabilities indicated above, as long as they have high credibility with you. (I'll leave it for you to imagine how you might respond if a Scout you perceive as more of an interloper gives unsolicited advice to you or your caregiver on a critical health issue.)

However, the ideal Scout may not be your caregiver, if their capabilities and emotional state make it a difficult color role for them to fulfill. Perhaps a trusted family member or friend might be more suitable in such a situation.

One other source of help with the Scout is cancer advocacy groups, particularly some of the more popular ones with well-established reputations and funding. Their professionals may be able to help you search or evaluate clinical trials.

Scout Color Role and Tint Interactions

Complementary color roles:

- Philosopher can support Scout, because it helps you develop evaluation criteria in the context of your life goals. For example, if quality of life is a higher priority than length of life, the treatment you choose may be less aggressive; or if staying local is a higher priority, you might not choose to travel for treatment, even if there are promising possibilities further afield.

Complementary tints: The Scout color role is more effective when performed with

- Optimism: Acknowledging that cancer research and treatments are always improving and a better treatment could be around the corner gives hope.
- Proactivity: Seeking out the best treatment for you, even if it's not what the first doctor you work with recommends, opens up your options to extend and improve your life.

Color roles that may conflict:

- Crisis Manager: Has a negatively complementary relationship with Scout, in that if you perform Scout effectively, you may have less need for Crisis Manager in the future.

- Warrior: The same negatively complementary relationship applies; if you're well-prepared for a treatment, you may have an easier time and won't require Warrior as much.

Scout Caregiver Connections
How to Help

Fulfill: Take the lead on researching options, presenting findings or discussing alternatives with physicians, or even making the treatment decisions for an incapacitated CC. As long as you keep the CC in the loop and have approval to broach any topics or treatments with the professionals, you can be a very effective Scout on the CC's behalf.

Partner: Share the Scout responsibilities such as the research, and suggest new alternatives that the CC hasn't discovered. You may also help assemble any research materials and attend all doctors' appointments too.

Support: Provide encouragement and a sounding board, even if you don't do any original research or advocacy. You may also show interest in the possibilities that the CC is researching and considering, and support extra efforts like "field trips" to other medical facilities, or direct contact with fellow travelers.

Bystander: Stay informed of any major initiatives or decisions the CC makes; to move from Support to Bystander, you can also "outsource" medical research to a third party such as another interested family member or a clinical trial matching service.

Potential Conflicts

Disagreement over how many treatments to try. Sometimes one partner may be tempted to try every possible treatment (e.g., all ordinary medical modes, plus a bunch of supplements) either simultaneously or in rapid succession, and the other wants to limit the treatments. It may be necessary to rein in the overzealous party on this one by limiting the treatments in play at any given time. Though it's normal to want to do everything possible to get the CC better, too many treatments at once can be exhausting to do, may make it difficult to determine which treatment is actually working, or could interact in undesirable ways (e.g., some vitamins inhibit the ability of certain chemotherapy compounds). As noted in the Patient chapter, you have to give the primary treatments time to work.

And always, always check with your medical professionals before exploring alternative options.

Try anything vs. insist on evidence. In some extreme cases, one party is so desperate for the CC's survival that they're willing to try anything, however implausible. I am disheartened when I see people traveling to some exotic location for a discredited treatment, or insisting that an aggressive cancer can be solved with some magic bullet, only to be bitterly disappointed when the course of action fails. The solution is for the other partner to gently insist on evidence of both the efficacy and side effects before wagering everything or going to extreme lengths to get a treatment that has been touted but not well vetted. I am not a doctor, and more power to those willing to consider less conventional treatments, but as the old saying goes, "Don't be so open-minded that your brains fall out."

Denial. Sometimes one party is in such deep denial about the need for research and action on the disease, that they're only able to cope day by day. In this situation it may be necessary for a third party medical professional or counselor to be brought in to help the CC and caregiver think at least a little more proactively.

Mutual Support

Acknowledge the difficult work of the Scout. Scout is probably one of the least-executed color roles of the typical CC; it's not only intellectually challenging for the layperson, but also emotionally overwhelming because it forces you to acknowledge that treatments can fail and that some conditions have a poor probability of survival. If the CC or caregiver is willing to plow through these challenges and take on the color role, they deserve a lot of credit from their partner.

Discuss your differences of opinion about treatments respectfully, especially in front of medical professionals. You don't have to act like twin robots when talking about treatment options with others, but it's not fair to turn the medical professionals into relationship mediators. Try to have your specific concerns and questions written down and agreed upon in advance. This will show your doctors that you have done your homework, have given thought to your actions, and are working as a team.

Quick Wins For the Scout

If you only have five minutes: Do a quick web search on your condition and see if any news about potential treatments for your disease pops up.

If you only have fifteen minutes: Ask yourself the simple question: "What am I probably going to be facing a month from now?" and write down a few action items for yourself that you can pursue to be better prepared.

If you only have an hour: Write down the known pros and cons of multiple treatment options you are considering, and do some background research or contact medical professionals to find better information on those pros and cons.

What Good Scouts Do

1. *Stay abreast of medical research and alternative treatment possibilities, but don't overdo it*
Cancer is a complex disease, but there is an explosion of promising new treatments coming on line all the time—not to mention the many types of complementary and alternative medicine (CAM) options to consider. It is probably in your best interests to scan the literature at least every so often so you are alert to new possibilities. All treatments should be of course run by the doctors first, as there may be interactions with the actions already planned.

However, it is possible to be so enthusiastic or even dogmatic about the information you've learned that you could alienate or undermine your partnership with your medical professionals.

2. Envision different scenarios and plan for them

It doesn't take a fortune-teller to realize that there are many possible paths ahead of you as you proceed through treatment. Surgeries can have unexpected complications. Chemotherapy might be more (or less) tiring than expected. New clinical trials may open up. You can have a recurrence. All of these events may require you to reconfigure your expectations as well as your work activities and personal life, so it's important to think about how you would handle such scenarios physically and mentally. What kind of support would you need, and from whom? I had to do a little scrambling when my own chemo treatments turned out differently from my expectations.

Chemosabes
posted by Andrew Trice, Monday, December 9, 2013

Chemo cycle 1 of 6 is now in the rear view mirror. Cycle two starts tomorrow.

Overall, the process so far has been less dramatic than I feared. It wasn't like I was Walter White from "Breaking Bad" sitting there in the recliner with a grim look on my face while toxic chemicals graphically invade my body in slow motion and freaky music plays in the background (followed, of course, by stumbling to the bathroom to "worship the porcelain God"). It was more like "Andy Banter: Medical Edition," wherein the protagonist breezily plops into the chair and proceeds to test the sense of the humor of a nurse who is sticking needles into him (hmm, is this a good idea?) while his wife tolerantly looks on and we then have an hour or so of quality time together (seriously, it's an upside of cancer treatment, the whole captive audience and twisted couple's date night thing).

This is not to say the chemo experience is all beer and Skittles; there does seem to be a physical law of some sort at work here along the lines of "every chemo action has an opposite and equally distasteful reaction." For instance:

Steroids given with chemo make chemo work better --> but then give you insomnia

Anti-nausea drugs given with chemo stop vomiting --> but stop other things too

Chemo lowers white blood cell count --> shot required to raise white blood cell count

Shot raises white blood cell count --> but causes bone pain and fatigue

OK, enough whining. Inverting the perspective by 180 degrees, there is also this to date:

Vomiting episodes: 0

Days of work missed: 0

Musical gigs missed: 0

Social events missed: 0

Hair follicles lost: Hard to tell (but who cares?) [Note to reader: I have been bald as an egg since the age of 27]

As my father used to say, even when I have bad luck, I have good luck. But we're not getting cocky; cycles 2-6 may wear me down progressively more, and we will deal with whatever comes, with aplomb.

That's a requirement for being a "chemosabe." The original Native American term "kemosabe" (that this is a play on) is of course from The Lone Ranger. "Kemosabe" is translated as "trusted scout" or "faithful friend." Like a scout should, I'll keep focusing on what lies ahead while also living in the moment as best I can, and reporting back to you, my own chemosabes, my faithful friends. Thanks.

---

3. Plan for treatment endings as well as beginnings

Even if it feels like a particular treatment regime will never end, I promise that it will. I was amazed at how fast a whole year went by as I passed through diagnosis, surgery, radiation, and chemo, all interspersed with clinical trial treatments. The next phase (including unfortunately, unexpected crises) is always sneaking up on you, so plan the logistics of that next phase as you're finishing up the current one.

4. Mix in fun and other important activities with treatment schedules

Unless your health situation is dire or you require urgent, unplanned treatments, find time to plan fun activities as well. This is its own important form of looking ahead; they're an important investment in your mental health, and give you something to look forward to. Your medical team will tell you how much flexibility you can build into your treatment schedule, and what you should be capable of in between cycles.

5. Go with the flow
No matter how hard you try, there are still going to be surprises to deal with, whether major or minor. Don't beat yourself up if you didn't anticipate every single possibility and have to adjust your course in mid-stream; planning isn't everything, and can sometimes cause more anxiety

6. Manage your anxiety: don't look too far ahead
As great as the Scout is, there is a big risk: you may so overthink your disease, your plans, and all possible future scenarios, that you experience "analysis paralysis." Sometimes scaling back to the "one step at a time" mindset is appropriate, because that's about as far ahead as you are able to think.

—⚬—

Moved in, one thing at a time
posted by Andrew Trice, Sunday, July 28, 2013
All:

I'm pleased to report that my digestive issues are becoming more and more manageable. All that really remains is building up weight and stamina; weight hasn't started moving back up yet, and I still need a ton of rest every day.

Several of you have drawn analogies to developmental processes in children (e.g., young children can often focus on building up one skill at a time, kids going through growth spurts need more sleep), and I think there's something to this. The hope is that to the degree my incisions and internal organs are healed up and basic digestion is no longer a monumental challenge, my body can move on to other goals, like becoming more robust and energetic. We'll see.

—⚬—

7. Decide on your preferred attitude towards statistics
Your Scouting may lead you to potentially discouraging information before it becomes reality, and that's not to everyone's taste. Some people want to know the statistical

data on side effects and complications, recurrence, survival, and so forth; others avoid them wherever possible. There's no right answer here. Only you can decide what you want to know and what you'd rather not consider at any particular time.

Knowing the data may prepare you for potential crises. Sometimes a CC or caregiver believes the CC is cured after treatment without realizing that recurrence is a possibility, and maybe a very likely one—and is blindsided when the recurrence happens. If you don't know the odds of these bumps, you can't predict their likelihood.

There is also a case for ignoring the data. First, every patient is different and you shouldn't assume that just because something is generally likely or unlikely, your experience will be the same. Additionally, the well-backed statistics are usually at least several years old, and the cutting-edge clinical trial information is probably not statistically significant yet. So if you choose not to trust the data, or think the data don't apply to you, you don't have to look at it.

Oncologists may or may not be straight with you about the odds; they're in a tough spot and don't want to discourage you. If you don't think you're getting the straight story on any particular point, you can choose to educate yourself, or not. My own approach is to view the data, but with skepticism.

Either way, as useful as the Scout is when you have the time and resources to pursue this color role, it has to be tempered and pulled back to the base camp from time to time. And when you return to your tent, you may need to stare into the campfire for a while and reflect on why you're there in the first place. That's the color role of the Philosopher, which we'll encounter next.

Further Reading on the Scout:

Beyond general resources such as the following, the websites of the advocacy and research groups for your specific cancer (e.g., Pancreatic Cancer Action Network) will be your best bet.

U.S. National Library of Medicine and National Institutes of Health, PubMed, http://www.ncbi.nlm.nih.gov/pubmed. NIH-sponsored website containing the latest research on cancer (and every other imaginable malady).

Jenny Marsh, ed., "Finding Your Cancer Cure: Your Basic Guide to Surviving Cancer," Energy Grid: Multi-Issue Alternative Media, accessed October 22, 2015, http://www.energygrid.com/health/cancer-cure.html. A guide to thinking outside the box on cancer treatment.

CHAPTER 10

The **Philosopher** Color Role: What Does This Mean?

T*he Mixed-Up Chameleon [children's book by Eric Carle] touches on at least three different philosophical topics, namely, happiness, change, and personal identity...*[22]

- **Philosopher at a Glance**
  - *Key Transformation:* from having simply *survived* (!) the cancer for a period of time, to *clarifying* your life priorities for the future
  - *Color:* **Pink** (think: faithfulness to purpose)
  - *Description:* Mull over big questions about the meaning and implications of the illness
  - *Most applicable when:* You have time for quiet reflection
  - *Strengths:* Provides a broader perspective on illness; encourages you to use time wisely
  - *Risks of neglecting:* Poor use of time and potential regrets
  - *Risks of overdoing:* Becoming morose, feeling emotionally paralyzed, or being overwhelmed

How the Philosopher Gives You Control

For most of us, the term "philosopher" conjures up the image of a frozen chin-on-fist nude figure not doing anything—and parents of philosophy majors often wonder

---

22 Tom Warternberg, "The Mixed-up Chameleon," accessed December 22, 2015, www.teachingchildrenphilosophy.org/wiki/The_Mixed_up_Chameleon.

what jobs their children can possibly get. But of course philosophy is not about "making a living," it's about figuring out what you're living for in the first place. If cancer doesn't make you into a philosopher, I don't know what could.

Philosopher forces you to clarify your values, to evaluate what is truly important to you—making it more likely you'll use your remaining time more wisely. It enables you to prioritize what to properly get upset about and what to properly let slide, freeing up more energy for handling the most pressing day-to-day challenges of the disease. Also, it gives you a better chance of using our remaining time more wisely, once we have greater confidence in what we'd really like to do.

If you don't enact the Philosopher, you are in danger of wasting the effective time you have left, whatever that may be. This in turn can lead to existential regret if your situation worsens, because cancer tends to make us ask the big questions. One common reaction to a cancer diagnosis is "Why me?" Scientific answers involving genetic variation, insidious viruses, or environmental conditions may not answer the question adequately. Looking to faith for an answer provides comfort to some and anger to others. From my perspective, "why me" is not the most important question; the implications of the illness are much more interesting and salient.

As you try to move away from the initial shock and anger of the diagnosis, your internal conversation may shift from "Why me?" to "Why go on?" And this is where Philosopher comes in. "Why go on?" is a much more actionable question; it moves you from bemoaning your situation to focusing on what you truly have to live for. Here are my early musings on this topic, recorded after my Whipple surgery but before I began radiation and chemotherapy:

The Median Isn't The Message (it'll just scare you at first)
posted by Andrew Trice, Thursday, August 22, 2013
All:
So in the midst of all the good news and a return to relative normalcy for a few weeks, I've recently had some time to study more scholarly articles and data on pancreatic cancer. This has led me into such abstruse (except to my quant colleagues at work) statistical areas as Kaplan-Meier Survival Curves, hazard ratios, log-rank

analyses, and multivariate analyses related to tumor characteristics. So, what would you think if I told you that, based on the most recent data I could find (from 2009), that the median life expectancy for someone like me is 17 months? Would that get your attention? I'm not making this up; this swag applies to someone who has had the Whipple procedure and the specific tumor characteristics on my pathology report.

Well, having made this calculation, why don't I just forget about work, take that round-the-world trip, and otherwise hit my bucket list in earnest? Well, it would scare the children, for one thing; really out of character for me to be extravagant. But in all seriousness, for solace we can turn to a marvelous essay by the redoubtable Harvard paleontologist (and baseball fan) Stephen Jay Gould. In 1981, Gould faced a cancer diagnosis with a median survival of eight months, yet survived for another 20 years. His essay reflecting on his experience, "The Median Isn't The Message," should be mandatory reading for every cancer patient who seeks hope after a challenging diagnosis.

In this essay, Gould records the internal conversation he had with himself about all the reasons he had to believe he would substantially beat the eight-month median, like his age, early cancer stage, quality of treatment, positive attitude, and so on. He then elaborates on his own disposition of strong purpose of proactivity to go with his positive attitude, and stresses how the conventional statistics are out of date and only cover standard treatment approaches.

I hope you can readily translate from Gould's circumstances to my own and see some potential parallels. To name a few, my treatment at Hopkins; the support of all of you; maintaining a positive attitude even when it's tough; and both the vaccine trial and other treatment improvements with the passing of time, neither of which are accounted for in the dataset I had.

So, yes, even though this is a damned dangerous disease we're dealing with here, we're still pressing on, planning for success, and not panicking. But that doesn't mean we don't have anything fun or special planned for the future either. I need to check whether my frequent flyer miles can be used for those flights to New Orleans for JazzFest next May....

Later, the Big Question that came up for me was even more action-oriented: "OK, universe, you got my attention with all of this medical unpleasantness. How do I maximize whatever time I have left?" Which in turn led me to the most important aspect of the Philosopher color role: discovering how to use my time wisely once I was more acutely aware that it was limited. Viewed in this light, cancer became a valuable forcing function that helped me cut through the daily clutter and distractions so endemic in our modern age and simply ask: what is really worth doing?

―――

Contingency Planning and Acting Across the Multiverse
posted by Andrew Trice, Saturday, March 29, 2014
....With all the status stuff out of the way, I'd like to turn to the topic of life planning under uncertainty. For this, I draw inspiration from the far-flung areas of quantum physics and financial planning.

In quantum physics, the multiverse is the hypothetical set of possible universes. People debate whether these different universes really exist, but one of the implications is that there may be multiple possible futures in store for us. One variable, of course, is the length of our remaining lifespans. Before this blog started, for me this number seemed like something I could reasonably estimate to be several decades, give or take a few years. Now, not so much.

In financial planning, a common technique to help you figure out your real goals is to ask yourself three hypothetical questions: a) what if I knew today that I had five years to live? b) same question, but five months to live? c) same question, but five minutes to live?

Putting all of this together, I conclude that since we can't ultimately predict or control what multiverse we will experience, the only thing we can control is how we plan and behave with different timeframes in mind. This includes both what we want to get done, and who we want to be. By taking this approach, we are best prepared for and responsive to whatever may come. Here's an idea of what we might consider across the three questions above:

Five years: This is the universe of major accomplishments and legacies, and is probably about as far ahead as most of us can look with much clarity. In this space, there is still time to take on another big job, write that book, help your children get to the next level of maturity and independence, or establish and maintain deep relationships.

Five months: This is the universe of the bucket list, of putting one's affairs in order, and of succession planning. In this space, we can plan and experience meaningful events and trips and other things we really meant to get around to, do estate and other legacy planning, and train and prepare those who will have to replace us when we can no longer fulfill our duties.

Five minutes: This is the universe that compels us to go to our emotional and spiritual cores. There's no time to do anything, except maybe say a few things and try to reconcile ourselves to our fate, loved ones, and Maker if you believe in one. What was left unsaid to those closest to me? What I have not let go of that I need to? Did I live life with zest, or just go through the motions? Will I be remembered as a nice and kind person, or a jerk? How do I respond to people in the moment, and particularly this one?

Plan and work across all of these various different timeframes, and you can't go wrong. Call this whole line of thinking "Contingency Planning Across the Multiverse"—now there's a pretentious label for the day. I'll be back in touch once we get results from the next scan in mid-April. Thanks and best wishes to all.

—⊶⊷—

Philosophizing is best suited to times when you can spend time in reflection, either alone or with others. There are advantages to both; alone, you don't have any distractions and may not feel pressured to "perform" while philosophizing with others gives you the opportunity to get outside perspectives. Either way, it's unlikely insights will come at moments when you're distracted.

—⊶⊷—

How You Staff the Philosopher

Philosopher is another color role that you have to take responsibility for, because it is all about values that are personal to you. That said, depending on the your temperament, you may need more or less help in enacting it .To the extent that you and your partner view your lives as a shared trek, you may choose to go through the planning process together. Opportunities for reflection with supportive friends and family may also add value to the color role, and life coaches and counseling professionals can provide objective expertise on the process if you need further help.

An ideal Philosopher has the mind of a strategic planner, able to formulate goals, understand the relationships between them, and translate those concepts into concrete plans. When this ability is coupled with self-knowledge and the ability to detect when a particular goal or course of action doesn't seem quite right, you are on solid ground for charting your course.

Philosopher Color Role and Tint Interactions
Complementary color roles:

- Scout supports Philosopher when you're evaluating possible treatments; Scout provides the research that tells you what is feasible in the context of the goals the Philosopher sets.
- Guru supports Philosopher because a key part of your life plan may involve clarifying what you'd like to give back to others.

Complementary tints: The Philosopher color role is more effective when performed with

- Mindfulness: Clarifying priorities while staying calm and focused enables you to apply your logic and intuition rather than just your emotions.
- Forgiveness: Forgiving yourself and others about what happened in the past enables you to move forward with plans for the future with fewer distractions.
- Passion: Having Passion enables you to explore your values with greater energy and confidence.

Color roles that may conflict:

- Actor and Crisis Manager: Both stand in opposition to Philosopher because they focus on immediate action.
- At the same time, in some sense the Philosopher color role provides a foundation for the whole palette; clarifying priorities affects how you respond in most of the other color roles too. In other words, no matter which color role you're taking on, it's important to balance thought and action. So this is not so much a conflict as a statement that other roles need to be tempered with Philosopher as much as possible.

Philosopher Caregiver Connections
How to Help

Fulfill: Because no one can tell another person how to live their life, Philosopher is not a mode which the caregiver can take over.

Partner: Take the initiative in scheduling less structured time together, and discussing what you'd like to do together in the future--whether that's "bucket list" items or broader lifestyle decisions, such as where to live or what retirement scenarios make sense for the two of you.

Support: Act as a sounding board and facilitator for the CC; listen actively and identify resources (books, professionals) that may help the CC clarify their own goals.

Bystander: Give the CC the space they need to do their own reflection. If this in turn gives you the space to play Philosopher for yourself, so much the better.

Potential Conflicts

Lack of interest in "inner life". Either because of natural temperament or stress brought on by the disease, the CC and the caregiver may discover that one partner is not interested in thinking through life priorities in any kind of systematic way. While it may frustrate the partner who is interested in deeper thinking about life issues (or vice versa), this approach reflects a philosophy in and of itself—usually the only way to finesse the difference is to adopt a "live and let live" perspective. But if the cause of the difference is that one partner has effectively checked out of the relationship or has given up hope for the future, professional counseling may be in order.

Mutual Support

Arrange a regular time and space for planning discussions. Playing Philosopher can prove challenging because it is easily put off. To improve the chance that the thinking and dialogue will take place, schedule a regular time when you can discuss your priorities and plans. This is something most healthy couples do already; the idea is to take time together to focus on longer-term issues.

Quick Wins For the Philosopher

If you only have five minutes: Identify one activity that you could either stop doing or get someone else to do because it's not a true priority for you. Perhaps you've been doing it out of habit, or a now-misplaced sense of obligation, or because no one else has stepped up. Make the decision to let it go.

If you only have 15 minutes: Brainstorm a "bucket list"; it can simply be fun activities, future accomplishments you want to aim for, or anything else that is meaningful to you.

If you only have an hour: Spend time reading a book about life planning, or in a meeting with a counseling professional. Often, a specialized cancer center in your area can help you identify resources for both.

What Good Philosophers Do

1. Think about meaning across different time frames
The journal entry above ("Contingency Planning Across the Multiverse") gives a sample of how one could go about this. Think about what you'd want to do if you had only a very short time, a modest amount of time, or an extensive amount of time.

This one is personal to me. After I got my diagnosis I realized (after I picked myself up off the floor) that a mature and complete response to this profoundly uncertain situation demanded that I think and act across all of these timeframes simultaneously. I should have been doing this anyway; I just didn't see it until I got hit in the pancreas. Everyone's answers to the above questions will be different, but if you want to leave this race having "left it all out on the track," you owe it to yourself to think flexibly about how you'd prioritize things under different scenarios.

2. *Use different apertures and perspectives to focus your thinking*

You can also look at your life from different angles to help you get an alternative perspective and inform your thinking. Ask questions like these: how do others perceive me and do I want to change that? What does integrity mean for me right now? Which of my behaviors would strike an objective observer as naive or misplaced, or otherwise flawed? If you can begin to answer these questions, you may find your definition of "the good life" changing. You may also want to consider doing some reading in the area of philosophy, or choosing novels that touch on philosophical issues.[23]

3. *Outsource non-essential activities to others*

After evaluating what's really important to do, if you can outsource things that you can't or don't want to do yourself, either paying others or getting volunteers to help, it frees up more time for other bucket list items and more substantial projects. This can include more family time, visits from friends, important occupational pursuits, legacy documentation (see the next best practice), or anything else that is especially meaningful to you.

4. Consider and write down legacy intentions

These items are often commitments you want to honor or tangible or intangible things you want to leave behind. Examples include projects you want to complete, ethical wills that pass along your values to future generations, charitable contributions, and estate plans. Writing these down forces you to think about what you want, and increases the probability that you will take actions to achieve them and ensure your wishes are honored.

5. Recalibrate goals as your condition changes

You cannot dictate the course of your disease. If you're in a stable condition, you may be wary and vigilant but can do normal activities at least for a while. However, if you become terminal, then your focus may shift radically to only doing the most critical things, which would typically including attending to unfinished business or simply

---

23 A side recommendation: if you do have spare time to refine your philosophical thinking and consider what is really important in the face of death, read the novella "The Death of Ivan Ilych" by Leo Tolstoy. (Hint: be like Gerasim, not Ivan)

focusing on enjoying life moment to moment as best you can. No matter what happens, you always have a choice about how you respond and what it will mean for your situation, so be open to changing your goals as you need to.

6. Talk over your philosophy with family or others in your support network

For many people, philosophizing is a team sport, not a solitary activity. If you need to talk out what you want to do with your life, by all means do so, especially if you have a close family member or good friend who can listen to you without becoming too emotionally involved. You can also employ a professional life coach or counselor for greater accountability.

On the other hand, no one can tell you how to live your life with cancer. However you enact the Philosopher color role, you have the opportunity to make thoughtful and positive choices that ring true for you.

It should be obvious that the Philosopher has its limitations as well. Figuring out what the good life is given your circumstances can be overwhelming, or even mentally paralyzing. In the end we all have to act in the world based on whatever productive thinking we do, so navel-gazing is going to have diminishing returns at some point.

And if you make good choices for you, others may very well notice too, and once you have established your goals, to the extent those goals can benefit others you have the opportunity to become a Guru as well.

—⊷⊷—

More Reading on the Philosopher:

Crystal L. Park, "The Meaning Making Model: A Framework for Understanding Meaning, Spirituality, and Stress-Related Growth in Health Psychology," *European Health Psychologist* 15, no. 2 (2013): 40–7, http://openhealthpsychology.net/ehp/issues/2013/v15iss2_June2013/15_2_Park.pdf. Makes the case that beliefs, goals, and a sense of purpose can make all the difference in what those with serious illness achieve.

Wendy Lichtenthal, prod., "The Process of Making Meaning from the Cancer Experience," Memorial Sloan-Kettering Cancer Center video, 19:00, 2011, http://www. mskcc.org/videos/process-making-meaning-experience. A short but powerful video presentation that can help you think through what is meaningful to you in the face of cancer. Produced by Dr. Wendy Lichtenthal, clinical psychologist at Memorial Sloan-Kettering Cancer Center.

CHAPTER 11

The **Guru** Color Role: I Hope I Can Help You

or the chameleon, the ability to identify with its surroundings is a defensive tactic that enables it to become virtually invisible when threatened. The correct use of the chameleon principle is to serve others, not oneself; employed appropriately, it reflects the degree to which the leader is capable of grasping the dreams, goals, needs, and concerns of every person within the organizational community. [24]

- **Guru at a Glance**
  - *Key Transformation:* from a period of *self-focus* due to the ongoing challenges of the disease, to a readiness to *contribute* to a purpose higher than themselves
  - *Color:* **Blue** (Think: tranquility and integrity)
  - *Description:* Serve as a role model and teacher to others through your response to illness
  - *Most applicable when:* You've had some time to reflect on your experience and want to turn your attention outward
  - *Strengths:* Allows you to make a fulfilling, positive impact on others
  - *Risks of neglecting:* Missed chances to serve others and "turn lemons into lemonade"
  - *Risks of overdoing:* Self-aggrandizement, inattention to your own health

---

24 M. Edward Krenson, "The Chameleon Principle of Leadership," Randolph School, September 2003, Accessed October 22, 2015, http://randolphschool.net/ftpimages/111/download/download_group1501_id23359.pdf.

How the Guru Gives You Control

If you're fortunate enough to survive cancer for a certain period, you'll probably notice something strange begin to happen; people start admiring you, holding you up as a role model, or even imbuing you with some sort of superhuman power. This can be both a blessing and a burden. A blessing, because your status gives you a tremendous opportunity to lead or help others; but a burden, because not every survivor wants attention, let alone additional responsibilities, or thinks what they have learned is valuable to others. Your initial response might be surprise or confusion—"Hey, I'm just trying to get well here."

But enacting Guru gives you another chance to expand your control over the cancer trek because it allows you to construct something meaningful and positive from whatever damage and suffering the cancer has inflicted. Suffering may understandably lead to a high level of self-focus; Guru is one way out of that.

When I talk about Guru I don't mean that you are a spiritual teacher per se. I mean Guru in the other sense of the word: that you act as an authoritative expert and role model who can serve others in some fashion[25].

This doesn't mean you need to have all the answers. And it doesn't have to be an "all or nothing" color role; you can start Guru as modestly as just helping one person in a small way.

In fact, a lot of Guru work takes place one-on-one. You can also act as a Guru for your support network or other circles writ large, whether you impart useful information informally or not. When I was playing Crisis Manager and Scout after my initial diagnosis, fellow cancer travelers played the Guru by giving me tips on what to expect with my surgery and treatments, identifying some best practices, and encouraging me. Since then, I have had the pleasure of speaking with a number of pancreatic cancer patients (excuse me, CC's) or their family members who were interested in my trek and wanted to see what they could learn from it.

---

25 If you are mainly interested in being a spiritual teacher, you could become an expert on the mindfulness tint discussed in a couple of chapters, or become a "Cancer Yoga" teacher, but I doubt that is the typical CC.

Any advice that you decide is worth sharing can be valuable; it doesn't have to be deep philosophical insights. You can simply share your experience, give those facing a similar procedure an idea of what to expect, or provide references to physicians, treatments, or other services you have found useful. You can also describe coping tools, mindfulness practices, or daily habits you have found beneficial in navigating your own cancer trek.

For example, when people asked me whether I was doing anything for my illness apart from conventional Western medicine treatments, I blogged my take on it. This in turn led to good conversations with others who shared their own experiences with me.

A CAM-do attitude

posted by Andrew Trice, Saturday, December 21, 2013
Some of you have asked what other things I'm doing to facilitate my healing in addition to all of the medical treatment. It's a very interesting question, and it gets us into the territory of CAM (Complementary and Alternative Medicine). When the patient opens up this particular box, a vast territory of additional options and practices are revealed. But which, if any, do you avail yourself of?

Philosophically, my inclination is to look at this scientifically if I can, while being open-minded to the idea that measures beyond those provided by the "standard medical model" may be beneficial. Plus, some CAM options have some good data behind them. Here's a couple of CAM areas I've thought about so far:

Diet and various nutritional and medicinal supplements--Tons of possibilities here, but apart from trying to eat lots of protein and calories within a balanced diet, I have pretty much steered away from doing anything extra. Why? Well, I figure that with all of the drugs I'm taking already and their various effects on my system, why introduce another variable into the equation at this point?

Body work / exercise--I'm pretty frustrated that I can't exercise vigorously these days, and I need another way to get my body to relax at the end of the day, so I've started a simple version of a practice called Yoga Nidra, which I have described to some as a "lazy person's yoga." Basically, you lie on your back in the "corpse position" (ok, scratch that thought) and focus on systematically relaxing parts of the body, along with the usual breathing focus common to so many varieties of yoga.

No exertion required, but it helps me relax and get to sleep. Can't imagine that any of this would interfere with all the medical measures I'm taking.

Finally, although they are not CAM practices as far as I understand, there are some other areas of practice that I think are equally important to my healing process as well:

Pet therapy--How can you be all wrapped around the axle with anxiety when you're petting your dog, who is making contented noises the likes of which you're not likely to hear this side of pornography?

"Service" therapy--Anyone facing a major illness or life crisis is familiar with its tendency to make one self-absorbed. The antidote to this is to remember to try to be more other-directed, whether that's continuing to work, helping and connecting with others directly, remembering them in your thoughts and prayers, and so forth. And amazingly, all of those things make you feel better about yourself.

I hope everyone has a lovely holiday break!

Finally, you can be a Guru in public. Some raise money for a particular area of cancer research. Others work with advocacy or counseling organizations, or change careers entirely to do something more meaningful to them. And some blog or write books (ahem), or do a mix of things. If you are working or volunteering and show your colleagues that you are handling your disease with equanimity, grace, or good humor, that's being a Guru too.

Whatever way you decide to enact the color role, give yourself some time after treatment to ease into Guru and to figure out what your niche for helping others is. On the other hand, just about any time is a good time to help others if you feel up to it.

If you decide that what you need to do for your own sanity is just "get back to normal" and not spend time thinking and talking about cancer anymore, that's fine too. However, in practice, I suspect few people come away from their experience not wanting to do anything to give back.

If you neglect to enact Guru, you'll miss opportunities to make something good come of the challenges of your cancer trek. That's not to say that you should feel guilty if you're not ready to advertise your availability to help others, but carefully consider it at some point when it feels right for you. Again, be guided by what feels right for your situation; you may find yourself directly approached for help.

How to Staff the Guru

Guru is very much like Philosopher, in that you need to decide what giving back means to you. There is space for others to meaningfully participate in this color role, however. For example, you can ask your support network to contribute to a specific cause by forming a team to run or walk in a fundraising event.

—◦◦◦—

Guru Color Role and Tint Interactions

Complementary color roles:

- Philosopher and Guru fit well together because while Philosopher answers the question "What is important?", Guru allows you to put some of your priorities in action, at least relative to helping others.
- Mortal and Guru fit together also, in the sense that Mortal helps you define what your legacy will be, while Guru enables you to act on specific aspects of your legacy.

Complementary tints: The Guru color role is more effective when performed with

- Passion: Exuding enthusiasm tends to prompt the same in others and inspires them as well.
- Optimism: Working on ambitious goals encourages you to work towards worthy goals that may be achieved in your lifetime, or later, so that they will still help others.

Color roles that may conflict:

- Patient and Warrior: Both of these color roles are more inwardly focused, and therefore don't naturally complement with Guru.

Crisis Manager: This color role has an intense, short-term focus, which would likely crowd out the Guru color role during a crisis.

Guru Caregiver Connections
How to Help

Fulfill: Because the CC needs to own the Guru themselves, as the caregiver you're not a player in this mode.

Partner: Engage in a joint enterprise with the CC, working next to them to raise awareness or funding, share expertise and advice, or otherwise contribute to a project that is meaningful to both of you. You help define the goals, take leadership on specific project segments, and collaborate with others as needed.

Support: Provide ad hoc support services to the CC just as you would for any other endeavors you'd help out with outside of the cancer trek. In this mode, you don't set the goals for or steer the Guru effort, but rather facilitate things or provide some of the pieces. Alternatively, simply tell the CC how you are moved or inspired by their contributions; the CC will often feel strengthened and energized by this.

Bystander: In bystander mode, you don't get involved in the CC's efforts or projects. However, if the CC isn't able or inclined to do Guru activities, but you are, you can also choose to be a Guru in your own fashion. Some spouses of CCs give advice to other people touched by cancer, providing their expertise one-on-one, in an open online forum, or even as a public spokesperson.

Potential Conflicts

Guru crowds out family or other priorities. It's great to make an impact on the world or be an inspiration to others, but you have to take care of priorities closer to home too. It doesn't make sense to save the world without first tending to your family. Worse, doing lots of outside activities can become a distancing mechanism, or an attempt to avoid the pain the family might be going through. Sometimes, our partners call us on our avoidance, and sometimes they are a party to it. Personally, I need to be careful not to take on more outside projects than I can handle, and instead to block out time to spend with my family--whom I treasure the most.

Mutual Support

Talk explicitly about how much Guru the two of you have in you and can afford. This is a color role which is particularly important to customize. If circumstances are dire or one of you doesn't have the temperament to be a Guru, put that on the table. Sometimes it's all you can do to focus on what's going on in your body or your home, and it's fine to acknowledge that. Listen carefully and respect each other if you have different perspectives on how much Guru will work for your partnership.

Quick Wins for the Guru

If you only have five minutes: Identify some small gesture you can make to another person in need; for example, send an email or call a fellow traveler or family member to check in.

If you only have 15 minutes: Make a list of projects you could feasibly do to help others, so you can revisit and reference it later when you have more time.

If you only have an hour: Spend an hour with a partner, friend, or counselor to help you prioritize any more ambitious Guru projects you are considering.

What Good Gurus Do

1. Customize the contributions you want to create

Unless you make Guru into a full-time career, you will probably have limited time to devote to the color role, so tailor it to suit your needs. Extroverts may want to help others one-on-one or raise awareness about their condition and the need for more research on its cure. Others may feel more comfortable working behind the scenes. The answer here lies with you. There will always be something unique about your own experience and the talents you can offer.

2. Approach and be approachable

I have often been struck by how many people need encouragement from fellow travelers or cancer survivors. You may initially feel reticent to reach out, but once you feel comfortable you can do a lot.

To overcome any uncertainty and awkwardness, it is often necessary to let people know that you are available. I am reminded of my experience as a dad of young children. I would come home after a business trip, and peek my head through the open front door. If I heard crying or yelling from Mom or the kids, I knew what the four magic words were: "How can I help?" Whether it's you or others who are in crisis, those words are simple yet powerful.

3. Maintain humility and balance

Being a Guru comes with its own set of risks. It's too easy to start believing your own press clippings when others praise you and hold you up as a model. If you receive the admiration of others, also realize that this comes with the responsibility to use your experience for good and not let your success and newfound wisdom puff you up. Additionally, be prepared for the possibility that your experience may not ring true for others, and that some with cancer might not have had the choices or survivor lifespan that you've been working with.

Balance in the practice of Guru is equally important. In the extreme, you could be so focused on playing Guru that you completely neglect your own health or other important priorities. But the problem is not always so simple. In some cases, an hour spent helping others might be an hour away from attending to your health or spending time with your family. In other instances, the impact is even less clear, like when helping others makes you feel better or gives you more energy than when you are with your family. Striking the right balance can be a continual challenge, but as long as you keep asking yourself what that balance should be, you won't stray too far off.

4. Acknowledge the help others have given you on the trek

Anyone who successfully completes a grueling course of cancer treatment knows that you can't do it alone. You learn to lean on people for all sorts of support--medical, emotional, and practical. This reflects both common sense and wisdom of all of the great spiritual traditions. Embrace this principle, give thanks for the help you receive, and share this simple insight with others.

Being a Guru gives you the chance to show leadership and compassion for others. Which you're going to need for taking on the final color role: confronting the ultimate challenge everyone on the planet faces as a Mortal.

Further Reading on the Guru:

As with the Actor, the answer here lies with your personal interests and inclinations. If you specifically want to give back to those affected with your variety of cancer, the advocacy groups for the various cancer types are a good place to start.

CHAPTER 12

The **Mortal** Color Role: Don't Be Afraid Of The Dark Places

*H*e was usually a bright coloured chameleon, blue, white, green, and yellow. But when he passed away, he went to very dark black or brown colour and from my understanding, this is the normal colour of a dead chameleon.[26]

- **Mortal at a Glance**
  - *Key Transformation:* from being *terrified* of disability and death, to *accepting* a range of possible outcomes
  - *Color:* **Black** (think: mystery and ending)
  - *Most applicable when:* in a terminal diagnosis, or planning for worst-case scenarios
  - *Description:* Confront and make peace with the frightening possibility that the illness may shorten your lifespan, perhaps dramatically; make peace with reality to the extent you can
  - *Strengths:* Promotes spiritual and emotional comfort and hope; helps you let go of anger
  - *Risks of neglecting:* "Unfinished business" left behind
  - *Risks of overdoing:* Becoming overwhelmed and beset with terror

---

26 "What Colour is a Dead Chameleon?" *Naked Scientists*, podcast audio, 2:00, December 18, 2011, http://www.thenakedscientists.com/HTML/questions/question/3268/.

How the Mortal Gives You Control

Let's not beat around the bush. Ultimately, cancer kills a lot of people before their time (or at least before what their life expectancy would otherwise be). Not all of us are going to make it to a ripe old age with cancer. Some surgeons call cancer "the enemy," and now, I know why. It is as frightening as hell when you think your expiration date is going to be moved up[27].

But here's the thing. By facing the possibility of death directly, you may find that death loses some of its power over you. I say "may" because I am not yet close enough to death to say how that statement is going to play out for me, let alone others. And I hope you don't have to fully enact the Mortal color role because of cancer. However, even though the Mortal color role is most salient towards end-of-life or when planning for worst-case scenarios, it is always appropriate to be as prepared as you can. No matter where you are in your cancer trek, there are tools that may help you confront the mystery of death and do yourself and your loved ones some good in the process.

Increasingly, physicians are focusing on the quality of the dying process for patients, and have provided us with great insights that can help us immeasurably in our final days. If you want a firm understanding of the medical and spiritual issues in preparing for end-of-life, I strongly encourage you to read two books.

How We Die by Dr. Sherwin Nuland, is a landmark book that discusses how we can better take control of our final days and even maintain some hope, not so much about mortality itself, but about "the meaning of what our life has been." Nuland's final chapters on cancer and lessons learned deserve to be read in their entirety.

A second, more recent book in a very similar vein is *Being Mortal: Medicine and What Matters in the End*, by Dr. Atul Gawande. Dr. Gawande also discusses the value of giving the elderly and dying more autonomy about their choices and living conditions at end-of-life. It's not always clear that more treatment at this phase is better. Particularly

---

27 It is also very disheartening and hard to accept when the cancer or its treatments doesn't kill you, but leaves you permanently disabled. For this scenario, the lessons in this chapter about acceptance and giving up control are still very applicable, but at the same time the cancer trek effectively continues and you can continue to use the full set of color roles to help you cope.

relevant for cancer patients, other recent research indicates that chemotherapy doesn't improve dying patients' quality of life.[28]

By enacting the Mortal color role, you have the opportunity to obtain comfort through your own degree of control over the dying process. Though, I'm not experienced in this myself, I appreciate the value of letting go at this stage: letting go of anger over the disease, of grudges long held against others, of regret for things done or not done, and of resistance to forces of nature no one can hold off forever. We are all trying to make peace with reality, which I pray I will be able to do when the time comes, but which I expect to be much easier said than done.

At the same time, I know it will be particularly hard to look after these issues if I'm overwhelmed by mental or physical pain, or worse, in a coma. All the more reason to face these matters up front and as best I can.

How to Staff the Mortal

It will come as no surprise that the CC must be the Mortal; everyone else is in support mode here, with you as the primary.

As you might imagine, people of faith may choose to work with clergy to get support on the spiritual dimension of the Mortal; many will seek the support of professional secular counselors as well. For the practicalities of estate planning and final arrangements, attorneys and funeral service providers obviously are experts you can draw upon. Finally, partners, families, and close friends act as sounding boards and help carry out your final wishes.

Mortal Color Role and Tint Interactions

Complementary color roles:

- Philosopher and Mortal are natural partners, in that they both have to do with meaning; however, the time orientation is different. Philosopher

---

28 "For Terminal Patients, a Round of Chemo May Be Harmful", Washington Post, July 28th, 2015.

explores meaning with an eye towards your remaining lifespan, whereas Mortal involves telescoping the time focus to end-of-life issues, while with looking back on what the meaning of that life was.

The reality of death is what drives both perspectives. It is in the background of our consciousness most of the time, but cancer puts it more into the foreground. M. Scott Peck, in *The Road Less Travelled*, suggests that we go a step further and make Death our ally and counselor: "With death's counsel, the constant awareness of the limit of our time to live and love, we can always be guided to make the best use of our time and live life to the fullest.[29]" Conversely, "when we shy away from Death, the ever-changing nature of things, we inevitably shy away from life."[30] If you assess that you have a lot of time left, the Philosopher color role may be more suitable; if time is a lot more limited, the Mortal color role should come to the fore.

Complementary tints: The Mortal color role is more effective when performed with

- Forgiveness: Applying Forgiveness is a key tool for enacting Mortal, because many of us are furious at the idea that this ride is going to end and that we won't get to do all the things we want to do.
- Optimism: Using this tint can be very comforting as well, because the hope that others will carry on your values and work after you are gone can sustain you at end-of-life.
- Mindfulness: Employing mindfulness practices may help you cultivate acceptance of a terminal diagnosis.

Color roles that may conflict:

- Actor: This color role would probably not be performed at this phase, because the existential nature of Mortal makes this period seem anything but "normal."

---

29 M. Scott Peck, *The Road Less Traveled: A New Psychology of Love, Traditional Values, and Spiritual Growth* (New York: Simon & Schuster, 1978), p.134.
30 Ibid, p. 134.

Mortal Caregiver Connections
How to Help

Fulfill: Because it's the CC's body and spirit involved here, you cannot meaningfully fulfill this color role on their behalf.

Partner: Give the CC your full attention and presence as they struggle with the universal problem of death and dying. It is a privilege to be around someone you love at these moments, and although you cannot solve their challenges for them, you can share in the experience and provide comfort through your presence.

Support: Provide or arrange for supportive care or hospice—indispensable for reducing the CC's suffering towards end-of-life. You can also provide input on or help facilitate any estate plans, moves to a more suitable dwelling for palliative care, or final arrangements. Though it will be difficult at times, stay calm and focused during this period if you can; it may help the CC retain emotional control.

Bystander: In bystander mode, you may <u>temporarily</u> choose not to engage in any Mortal issues for a certain period, remaining detached from the reality that the CC is near end-of-life. This may be a functional self-protection mechanism (Mortal can be as overwhelming for caregivers as for the CC); at other times it may constitute denial or inability to complete unfinished business with the CC.

Potential Conflicts

Disconnects in how the two process a terminal diagnosis. Processing end-of-life issues is very personal and not everyone is in the same place at the same time. It's possible that the two of you may be in different places at any given time. One partner may exude calm and acceptance, and the other denial or anger. Or one partner may take a very matter-of-fact view of the whole thing, while the other is paralyzed with fear and otherwise not ready to make final preparations. Professional help may guide you through the process together. Additionally, you may want to allocate end-of-life preparations to the action-oriented person—as long as the other partner doesn't object or disagree.

Mutual Support

Be exquisitely gentle with each other, and get others to help. There is no more difficult issue to confront than the reality of your own death, and the second biggest issue is the death of the one closest to you. If one of you isn't ready to have the conversation about death, be hesitant about pressing the issue too much with them alone; a confrontation is the last thing you want with your loved one at this sensitive time. Instead, strongly consider bringing in the professionals, like grief counselors, clergy, and others who help individuals and couples deal with end-of-life issues.

Ask, and follow up on the "breadcrumbs" your spouse would like you to leave behind. If you have the time and energy, it is very useful to think hard about what documentation the CC can leave behind to make living life easier for the remaining family. I have done some pretty detailed thinking about this topic, which I call "breadcrumbs":

—∞∞—

Breadcrumb Love

posted by Andrew Trice, Saturday, December 14, 2015

Having just marveled that I'm still around, I wanted to turn to the serious question of what to do under the assumption that someday I won't be around. It may sound odd or even morbid, but one of my main vehicles for staying sane and feeling in control the last 2 1/2 years has been an almost obsessive focus on how to help my family carry on and live their lives as smoothly and effectively as possible should I be unavailable.

My purpose is not to attempt to minimize or short-circuit the grieving process all of us go through when we suffer loss, but to do as much as possible to provide the documentation, support, and guidelines I think my family will need and treasure in my absence. We can't prevent the pain of loss, but perhaps we can reduce the trauma of having to live life after that gaping hole opens.

I think of what I'm leaving behind as a trail of breadcrumbs my loved ones can follow to help them figure out where they need to go more easily. I like the breadcrumb metaphor because crumbs are not enough for true sustenance or peace, but they can give people some direction. You might call this "breadcrumb love"--something that may seem insignificant in the larger scheme of things, but nevertheless shows loved ones that you truly cared and tried to be thoughtful about how you can help them carry on. I've been building my breadcrumbs up bit by bit, at three levels (to address the same fundamental issues I focus on in my book, by the way):

The everyday coping level: documenting financial records and completing estate plans, assembling lists of repair people and other professionals we use, showing the family where all the various supplies are stored, cross-training the family on the routine tasks I do for the household, delegating some things I've done myself in the past, de-cluttering so stuff is easier to find

The life management and decision making level: recruiting a "kitchen cabinet" of trusted advisors accountable to help my wife in domains with major financial or lifestyle implications with which she feels she would appreciate help (e.g., car repair and purchase, computer stuff, staying engaged socially). Put another way, I have found people she knows she can call on who could sit around that kitchen table with her and stand in for me as a trusted and capable sounding board when an important discussion or decision needs to take place. I've done the same on a smaller scale for the girls.

The legacy and life lessons level: Writing an ethical will and a set of life lessons I want to impart to the girls, writing special messages to the girls to be given to them at significant moments in their futures, recording podcasts so no one will have to preserve my voicemails just to remember what my voice sounded like (and coupling this with personal messages to each person in the family and a bit of oral history), recording videos to add to the visual component of my memory, designating suggested recipients of bequests and memorial contributions.

The nice thing about all of this is that it's a set of practices worth doing even if you aren't facing a life-threatening illness. It helps you be better organized, plan for contingencies less dire than death (e.g., temporary sickness, need to be away from the family for an extended period), and provides snapshots of the state and principles of your life that someone will treasure someday (possibly far in the future). The end of a year is a good time to take stock and think about longer-term issues; I hope folks will consider making a start or continuing with some of the above items if it seems useful and appropriate.

Quick Wins For the Mortal

If you only have five minutes: Jot down a few major accomplishments or qualities you'd like to be remembered for. This can be used to guide other Mortal activities later.

If you only have 15 minutes: Make a list of the practical things you could work on to help your successors take over your commitments at home, work, or elsewhere.

If you only have an hour: Spend an hour with a counselor, clergyperson, or estate planner to help you work through a practical, emotional, or spiritual issue related to the Mortal color role.

What Good Mortals Do

1. Act alone, but avail yourself of help

One of the most relevant speakers on the perspective of the Mortal color role is Dr. Roger C. Bone, who himself died of cancer in 1997 and advocated for terminally ill patients. In his primer, "A Dying Person's Guide to Dying,"[31] he reminds us that dying is "a journey one takes alone with a crowd;" that is, if you are dying, you have to make

---

31 Roger C. Bone, "A Dying Person's Guide to Dying," *Hospice* (American College of Physicians, 1997), Accessed October 22, 2015, https://www.hospicenet.org/html/dying_guide.html

the decisions about your care and your legacy (and when you are "done") yourself, but the help of others is indispensable.

This makes perfect sense, because being a Mortal is too scary to take on completely alone. Ask the people who feel right to you--whether that's clergy, counselors, your spouse or partner, or close friends-- to go with you to the dark places and make the process seem a little less scary.

Although this is way above my pay grade, I'll also point out that many people find solace in their faith tradition at end-of-life,[32] and leave the details of how you process that between you, your family, your spiritual advisors, and your Higher Power (if any).

2. *Give up control gracefully*

There's no getting around the fact that in the end, everyone gives up all control of their capabilities, and more than in the other color roles Mortals have the difficult task of trying to accept help graciously and gratefully. This help may come from family and close friends as well as medical professionals, or from unexpected sources like people you have only a vague connection with who take an interest in your situation. Whatever the source, do your best to be grateful.

Even before the end, you may reach a point when "being" is more important than "doing" anything in particular. Armed with the knowledge that the time is coming when we can't do anything, we can simply focus on appreciating existence and connections with others.

3. *Think through final arrangements and advance medical directives*

Most of us really don't want to think about these issues, but somebody will eventually have to address them. If it feels right for you to plan out the details of your funeral and disposition arrangements, doing so now will reduce the burden on your family. And taking care of the medical side of end-of-life by creating and distributing a living will or advance medical directive can ensure your wishes will be followed.

---

32 See, for example, Allison L. Allmon, Benjamin A. Tallman, and Elizabeth M. Altmaier, "Spiritual Growth and Decline Among Patients with Cancer", Oncology Nursing Forum 40, no. 6: 559-565.

Funeral arrangements, life insurance beneficiaries, and heirs (no matter how big or small the fortune) are decisions that everyone, not just cancer patients, can benefit from discussing with close companions. It also may give your survivors some peace to know that the way you are memorialized is consistent with what you really want. You cannot spare your loved ones grief and pain when you die, but if there's anything you can do to reduce the trauma they feel, that's well worth doing, in my opinion.[33] 'Nuff said.

4. Consider continuity of household operations
One of my greatest fears is that my wife will get up one day after the initial shock of grieving and start asking practical questions, like: What are the bills? How will I pay them? How do I do our taxes? How do I service the car? To the extent you can, write down details of all of the records you keep and the household activities you cover, so that your family won't be scrambling when you're not available. This is also a best practice if you don't have a terminal diagnosis, but know you're going to be out of commission for a while, as with a major surgery.

5. Try to help others be at peace with your illness and mortality
Dr. Bone points out that sometimes the hardest part about dying is the effect it has on your family and friends. Helping them handle your death can be part of the final gift you give them. One critical step in this process is talking openly with loved ones about the likelihood your illness is terminal.

He also speaks about the delicacy of dealing with your loved ones' reaction to the news. Some people may be shocked and withdraw, others may feel the need to fill up your time with activity and companionship that you may not always want. All of this is understandable and even expected, but you should still claim control over how you spend your time and whom you spend it with.

6. Think about how you want to say goodbye
Another eloquent and inspiring authority on the Mortal color role is Randy Pausch, author and presenter of the book and viral video "The Last Lecture." Pausch, who

---

33 There are plenty of examples of famous people leaving their affairs in disarray. Picasso died at the age of 91 without a will, even though he realized that settling his estate would be an absolute nightmare. Lots of trauma and hassle for the heirs; not the way I want to go.

died of cancer in 2008, understood the power of facing death squarely and milked everything he could from every single minute once he received his terminal diagnosis.

Just as importantly, as a father of young children Pausch focused intensively on creating memories for those children and his wife in his final months, trying to imagine what he would want his children to remember about him and how his spirit could best live on through them. This surely provided him with a measure of comfort as he passed on, with a minimum of "unfinished business." I was so impressed with this that I have also composed a number of written, audio, and video works that my loved ones can turn to when I'm no longer around.

I would encourage you to think about saying goodbye not only in terms of making final arrangements, but of engaging in meaningful individual or group encounters before you may be too drugged or in too much pain to do it in a meaningful or coherent way. Take the time to meet with the important people in your life--old friends, good work colleagues, extended family --in a way that is right for you.

—<small>◦◦◦</small>—

Further Reading on the Mortal:

Randy Pausch with Jeffrey Zaslow, *The Last Lecture* (New York: Hyperion Books, 2008); Randy Pausch, "The Last Lecture: Achieving Your Childhood Dreams," YouTube video, 1:16:26, from a lecture at Carnegie Mellon University, posted by Carnegie Mellon, December 20, 2007, https://www.youtube.com/watch?v=ji5_MqicxSo.

M. Scott Peck, *The Road Less Traveled: A New Psychology of Love, Traditional Values, and Spiritual Growth* (New York: Simon & Schuster, 1978).

Sherwin Nuland, *How We Die: Reflections On Life's Final Chapter* (1995; repr. New York: Random House, 2010).

Atul Gawande, *Being Mortal: Medicine and What Matters in the End* (New York: Metropolitan Books, 2014).

CHAPTER 13

The Chameleon Tints:
Making It All Better

If you look at the skin of a chameleon, you find that they have several layers of specialised cells called chromatophores and these are cells that can change colour. On the outer surface of the chameleon, the skin is transparent and just below that is the first layer of these cells, and they contain various pigments [which change the tint of the color]...[34]

Each of the color roles we've discussed provides a distinct perspective on how to navigate through cancer. However, there are a number of other tools, or "tints," that cut across all nine of the color roles because they can be used to improve your experience at almost any point in the cancer trek. The seven tints we'll cover in this chapter are humor, passion, mindfulness, optimism, proactivity, relationships, and forgiveness. With apologies to Stephen Covey, think of these as the seven habits of highly effective cancer patients. Most of these are personal qualities to cultivate and maintain, though you can obtain assistance in applying them.

Applying the tints can improve your CC performance by making it easier to enact a particular color role (for example, using a sense of humor with a medical professional while a Patient to make interactions and procedure more enjoyable or less unpleasant). It can also be a key part of the transformation the color role enables. For instance, mindfulness is a key tool that the Crisis Manager uses to move from being overwhelmed to instituting a plan to move forward. No matter how you apply

34   University of Cambridge, "How and Why do Chameleons Change Colour?", Accessed December 22, 2015, http://www.thenakedscientists.com/HTML/questions/question/2634/

them, the tints make the enactment of the basic color roles more pleasing and productive for you.

1. Humor

While you might think cancer is no laughing matter if your own life is in danger, cancer is also apparently so funny to so many people that there is a whole sub-genre of books about it (my personal favorite titles: *What About the Hair Down There?* and *Crazy Sexy Cancer Tips*). And Norman Cousins' landmark work *Anatomy of an Illness as Perceived by the Patient* speaks much more eloquently and extensively about the connection between laughter and healing than I ever could, so I won't attempt to add to that body of distinguished literature. However, I can say that when you think about how humor can help you, look for comedy in at least three specific areas relative to the CC color roles.

First, there is humor as a direct, conscious healing strategy within the Patient color role. In essence, make yourself laugh to heal better. This was the strategy Cousins used during his illness, when he forced himself to watch a bunch of Marx Brothers movies while facing a very poor prognosis. I distinctly remember having some visitors during my hospital stay who made me laugh so hard I had to tell them to stop because my abdominal stitches were hurting so badly. But that's a trade I would still make today.

Second, you can find humor in the many absurd situations associated with treatment regimes, which can lighten up the Warrior in you. Think about the comedic possibilities in pain, indignities, irony, or loss or subversion of bodily functions. By laughing about misfortunes like this, you ultimately transcend the humiliation. Here is a blog entry I made along those lines.

World's Worst Cancer Treatment Music
posted by Andrew Trice, Tuesday, October 15, 2013
And he's coming around the back stretch of the radiation treatment track...evincing some fatigue and digestive upset but still moving apace....only eight more treatment lengths to go.

That's the summary of current status; now onto the really fun part.
WARNING: Very Dark Humor ahead.

———◦◦◦◦———

So yesterday, I enter the laser beam room and they're playing Michael Jackson. They pipe Pandora into the room and you get to pick the channel you want to listen to during your zapping treatment. Usually I pick a jazz channel, but for a change of pace I tell them to keep Michael on (he was so sensitive you know...)

The treatment starts, I say my usual prayer of thanks for the life-extending, technologically advanced therapy, and Michael's song ends. Then another song starts:

(Bass) "Doop Doop Doop", "Another One Bites the Dust" (repeat)

"And another one down and another one down, another one bites the dust..."

[Abrupt pause in music]

(Technician, over PA): "Sorry about that, Mr. Trice..."

[Elevator music starts up]

———◦◦◦◦———

In retrospect, the biggest danger was not me taking offense or getting depressed, but of me convulsing with laughter and the beam hitting the wrong spot because I couldn't stay still.

However, this got me to thinking: is there a more extended playlist of tunes that shouldn't be played for cancer patients? Here's my initial list to add to Another One Bites the Dust:

1. "King of Pain" by The Police. Self-explanatory.
2. Theme from "Six Feet Under," an HBO series about a funeral home. Very eerie.
3. "The End" by The Doors. A real dirge.
4. "Turn, Turn, Turn," by whomever covers it. "A time to be born, a time to die...."
5. Most 20th-century classical music (the discordant and chaotic stuff).

6.	"Ready to Die" by The Notorious B.I.G. A profanity-laced, utterly despondent rap. The natural consequence of a life of crime and gang membership.

7.	"Knockin' on Heaven's Door" by Bob Dylan. Dylan has a naturally dirgy voice anyway.

8.	"(Don't Fear) The Reaper" by Blue Oyster Cult. Who needs to be reminded of that guy?

9.	"Fade to Black" by Metallica. Depressing as The Black Hole of Calcutta.

If you have your own entries, send them in and maybe I'll include the collection in a future post. I'm impossible to offend.

—⊗—

Third, humor can be a means of communication within the Publicist color role. Here, the strategy is to convey your situation in a light and entertaining way, which puts your support network at ease and relaxes you too. In some cases it can even become its own outlet for well-being. Here is a blog entry I did in that spirit; a mock quiz about my illness, treatment, and condition.

—⊗—

Boring is Good; Gag Quizzes are Better, Your Support is Best
posted by Andrew Trice, Wednesday, February 12, 2014
Hello friends, I know that all of you in the DC area are hunkering down in anticipation of the snowstorm, so it seems like a good time to check in. Several of you have asked why I haven't posted for quite a while (over three weeks, actually) and the answer is that there hasn't been much on the medical side to report on. I'm just grinding through the chemo treatments (75% done now) and my condition, energy, ability to work and play music, weight, blood tests, etc. are all pretty much the same. In this phase of the treatments, boring is good. We foresee no new potential drama points until the next CT scan when chemo is done just over a month from now.

But I can't just do a short, boring post and stop there; to do that would be to compromise my blog brand. So to entertain you a least a little bit, try your hand at answering the following questions:

1. The cost of each chemo pill Andy takes is:
    a) $35 for the insurance company, $1.25 for me
    b) Firstborn male child (ha ha, drug company suckers, I don't have any male children)
    c) Free, as part of my vaccine trial
    d) $35 for the insurance company, pennies for me because of a discount program

ANSWER: a). I tried for d), but they rejected me.

2. The most humiliating comment or suggestion directed at Andy about his condition is:
    a) "You're drinking Ensure? Isn't that the stuff they force feed to prisoners?"
    b) "You've got to have a scooter if you want to visit Disney World."
    c) "Aren't you just buying time?"
    d) "Boy, you've really got that hobo look going with that loose clothing."

ANSWER: None of the above, I'm beyond humiliation and people have been incredibly non-humiliating. And only a) actually occurred, b) may be a very good idea, but c) actually did happen to another pancreatic cancer patient I'm in contact with. With friends like that....

3. The consensus is that Andy's most appealing body part right now is
    a) His veins
    b) The shape of his bald head
    c) His guns
    d) His piano hands

ANSWER: a) and b). Guns aren't doing so hot with the weight/muscle loss.

4. People tell Andy he "looks good" all the time, with the unspoken qualification of...
    a) "for someone with a cancer with such dispiriting survival statistics."
    b) "for someone with two teenage daughters."

    c)   "for someone with no digestive system."

    d)   "for a geezer who is all skeleton and no fat."

ANSWER: I don't know. Do I look like a mind reader?

5.   Neulasta is...

    a)   A recently introduced ED drug

    b)   An $11,000 per dose shot Andy gets to boost white cell counts

    c)   A miracle drug that prevents immuno-suppression and keeps Andy working

    d)   A nerve gas antidote.

ANSWER: b) and c). Luckily I have a discount program for the shot so I pay $30.

6.   Andy's chance of surviving five years or more is

    a)   a) 15%; go with the published stats

    b)   b) 100%; he's a medical miracle buttressed by tremendous spiritual support

    c)   c) 25% or more; the vaccine and other new treatments will help

    d)   d) Who the hell knows? Just live every day to the fullest and don't worry about it.

ANSWER: Depends on the day.

Finally, just a thanks to all of you for continuing to check on me, help me, and pray for me. That's always the best part of all of this.

———☦———

And don't be afraid to indulge the urge to tease your support network either, like on the topic of your weight loss during radiation or chemo:

———☦———

posted by Andrew Trice, August 22, 2013

Thanks to the legions of you who have offered to "give" me some of their excess pounds so that I can gain them. If only it were feasible given current technology and cultural norms. But I have decided that the real future in cancer treatment is not in cutting-edge gene therapy or immunotherapy breakthroughs. No, it's in fat transplant procedures from friends and loved ones that reverse weight loss and cachexia in the patient. There's just so many willing donors out there, we've got to figure out a way to give the public what it wants.

—◦◦◦—

Whichever modes of humor are your preference, do something about it. Don't make cancer into a sacred cow. Make it funnier.

2. Passion

If you had good reasons to get up in the morning before you got cancer, keep them going as best you can, and find new ones too. It is not a secret that people with a passion for something feel and often do better than those who don't. Whether you're really into family activities, love your job, have a great hobby, or feel enthusiastic about a cause you believe in, anything that gives you a spark of energy is going to help you.

First, you can enhance your performance as an Actor by playing out your passion. If an activity felt good before you had cancer, it's going to be even more meaningful after you become ill, because you'll appreciate it even more. After I was diagnosed, I made a conscious effort to listen to, create, and play more music than I had before, and I think it greatly facilitated my healing process.

—◦◦◦—

Music and Healing: the untold story
posted by Andrew Trice, Tuesday, September 10, 2013
While things are still quiescent on the treatment front (radiation starts next Tuesday, the 17th), I'd thought I'd do a post or few about some other facets of this whole experience that I hope are of interest. For instance, knowing my passion for playing the piano, many of you have asked about the role music has played in my recovery to this point. Short answer: a very powerful role, facilitated greatly (as with so many other facets of this trek) by many of you.

You may recall that 3 days after surgery, my brother walked with me down to the piano in the hospital lobby, and I had my first experience playing piano with an IV in. That was a real rush, and it was just one example of "music therapy" that I was fortunate to experience (albeit the one with the best photo op). Here's some other good ones:

- Listening to music on my electronic devices through the hospital stay, for relaxation, inspiration, and sheer pleasure. I never turned on the TV the whole stay; it just didn't seem life-affirming in the way the music is for me. One time I was so wrapped up in listening to a jazz piece (complete with playing the "air drums") that an orderly came in without me noticing and was mouth agape at this crazy patient.

- Including "musical milestones" on my goal chart that I put up in my room. When do I get to play in public again? When am I scheduled to play for the temple? When do I get to practice with my big band again? I've got to get better so I can hit these dates!

- Appreciating music during those first few critical weeks at home. Sometimes listening to music was about the only thing I could do during the worst of the discomfort and tiredness, and while it didn't make the difficulties go away, it was always something to hang onto and staved off loneliness and negative thoughts.

- Sharing music with me. Some of you also gave me sound mixes and suggestions about cool new things to listen to, which was very helpful. Others came over and played music with me during my recovery, or transported my piano to a practice session for me. One of my clergy sang a song for me while I was in the hospital, another made sure I was engaged with all of the planning and practicing for holiday services. So there was a community element to all of this too that I really appreciated.

- Inspiring me to continue my creative process. Since returning home and feeling well enough, I've had the chance to practice and to continue composing a bit. You have a different perspective after going through something like this, and I can feel it in the stuff I'm composing and improvising to now--a kind of lightness and thankfulness, I suppose.

OK, that's a long enough post. Go listen to some music, everybody.

Second, a Philosopher color role played with passion results in peace of mind about the future, at least the parts that you can control. There is nothing like taking on the challenge of "living on purpose" when you are more acutely aware that life is limited. For me, my Philosopher was activated once I knew I might have lifespan issues.

Third, applying passion to the Guru color role allows people to help others in ways that they never thought possible. Those who raise awareness or money for cancer causes (for example, Canadian runner Terry Fox, or major underwriters of pancreatic cancer research) come to mind. Some Gurus go in new directions they would not have attempted prior to diagnosis, such as working with other cancer patients as a new career.

Finally, remember that you don't have to make grand gestures or do some major project just to exude passion. You can just enjoy your family and work more. Doing things with passion seldom has a downside.

3. Mindfulness

In recent years there has been a surge of interest in using meditation and similar focusing techniques to further healing of cancer and other illnesses. Based on an emerging body of research[35] and my own experience, I would commend this general approach. Any mechanism that helps to induce greater self-awareness, calm, or broader consciousness can be valuable. It doesn't so much matter whether that is obtained through meditation, yoga, visualization or just taking the time to reflect on things systematically; all can improve your mental or physical state. These effects can be felt in the context of at least three color roles.

Many people find comfort in their mental and spiritual mindfulness practices during times where the Patient color role is in the foreground. In her "Cancer Warrior" memoir, Ruth Levin describes intense visualization exercises in which she pictured her tumors being destroyed and healthy tissue radiating light and health in their place.

---

35 See, for example, Cecile Annette Lengacher, et al., "Mindfulness Based Stress Reduction (MBSR(BC)) in Breast Cancer: Evaluating Fear of Reoccurrence (FOR) as a Mediator of Psychological and Physical Symptoms in a Randomized Control Trial (RCT)," *Journal of Behavioral Medicine* 37, no. 2 (2014): 185–95, doi:10.1007/s10865-012-9473-6; and Christina Shennan, Sheila Alison Payne, and Deborah R. Fenlon, "What is the Evidence for the Use of Mindfulness-Based Interventions in Cancer Care? A Review," *Psycho-Oncology* 20, no. 7 (2011), 681–97, doi:10.1002/pon.1819.

In my own case I've done both yoga and meditation, as well as writing, which can be its own form of meditation (as could drawing, or other forms of artistic expression). Writing in particular helped me to clarify what I needed to do for self-care and view the state of my health objectively.

As a Crisis Manager, you may use mindfulness as a mechanism for calming yourself down and clearing your mind to make space for new possibilities and solutions. Mindfulness also allows you to observe your feelings of terror without necessarily giving into them. I have a vivid memory of talking to one of my clergy during a post-diagnosis panic; he told me that there are always goals that can be reached during the trek, even if they aren't the goal of total cure everyone is looking for. That really calmed me down and made me realize that cancer was something I could live with.

When you're enacting Philosopher, mindfulness can help you make decisions about the direction you want to take your life. For example, after a period of reflection following a clear CT scan I concluded that I needed to take a break from blogging to focus on longer-term priorities, like writing this book. Now that the intensity of the treatment had abated it felt like I could move on without folks worrying too much about me.

Happy Hiatus

posted by Andrew Trice, Wednesday, April 23, 2014

I hope everyone had a good spring break, Passover, Easter, whatever applies to your particular situation. I've been having a very good time myself, between the first Passover Seder in our new place, a vacation at Walt Disney World, and most significantly, another clear CT scan. Yes, as we had hoped for, I got official notification today that I have survived the most recent elimination round in the Hopkins vaccine tournament.

So on Friday, I'll enjoy the distinct privilege and high honor of getting stung six times again with this esoteric cocktail of genetically engineered cancer cells for my immune system to rebel against, and I'll get monthly booster shots through

July as well. At 11 months after diagnosis with this diabolical disease, the probable survival horizon continues to expand further into the future.

Several of you have asked me: what exactly is the status of the cancer at this point? Well, we certainly can't say I'm cured; recurrence still remains a very dangerous possibility. But what the scans and other tests say is that there is no visible or specific evidence of the disease in my system right now--the nurse says that "stable disease" is a good label for where I'm at. An appropriate cautionary label, because "absence of evidence" is not necessarily "evidence of absence"; the cancer is probably still lurking in a number of places at the microscopic level, and if so that's what the vaccine is intended to fight against.

But with all that said, right now we are in a very good place that I am very grateful to be in. After all of the surgery, radiation, chemo, and vaccines, we are moving into a "maintenance and surveillance mode" on this disease.

Which gives me the pleasure of making another announcement: it seems like the right time for me to be removed from what I fondly call "the DLs" (disabled lists). At the risk of tempting fate, I am saying that it is ok and seems appropriate for me to be removed from the formal prayer lists at churches and synagogues that so many of you have kindly placed me on. As any of us would, I retain the option of going back on the lists later if necessary. Thank you so much for all of your support and prayers since diagnosis.

---

4. Optimism

When I talk about optimism in the context of cancer, it is not blind optimism. It is a realistic, clear-headed optimism; it is about acknowledging the range of outcomes that can occur yet planning, working, and hoping for success. No matter what your situation, there is room for optimism.

Human beings have the unique ability to change their perspectives and thereby their moods and actions, no matter what their circumstances. Whenever you can, choose to "make your own weather" rather than spiral into despair. I understand that saying this doesn't make it easy, but it's worthwhile to give some thought to what optimism and success mean in your particular context. For example, on a particular day, you might look forward to the success of making it through a hard day's treatment. Even if you are nearing end-of-life, there is optimism in the opportunity to spend quality time with family. The difference between the outside world's definition of success and your own internal measure of success, is especially obvious when you consider how the optimism tint plays out in three of the color roles.

At the border of the Crisis Manager and the Scout, optimism means doing everything you can to achieve the results you hope for, and rallying your troops to get the help you need. This was my situation when I was trying to think through what might happen after I got home from surgery. For all I knew, I wasn't going to make it out of surgery, but that wasn't going to stop me from planning future goals like moving into our new place.

As a Warrior, use optimism to visualize a day when your capabilities will extend far beyond what you can handle now, even if you're hurting and can't do a fraction of what you're used to doing. I was feeling like, well, crap barely a week away from the operation, but I was getting great care and visits, and believed my doctors and my internal compass that things would eventually get better.

Strong end to the week
posted by Andrew Trice, Friday, July 12, 2013
Hello all, hope you are looking forward to the weekend. Back here at the Healing Hut, I'm pleased to report that we've been steadily improving since my return home Tuesday:

Healing and Pain: need half of the pain meds I needed at the end in the hospital, and managing the timing of it better (hit the wall a couple of times earlier). It no longer hurts much to laugh or cough, so bring on the jokes and the hernia exams.

Mobility and Range: up to 15 min power walks at a stretch, navigating steps no problem, flexibility increasing notably.

Food Intake and Digestion: up to about five small meals/day, appetite increasing and digestion easier; this new machine I've got sometimes sputters and is cantankerous, but it's getting on the right track.

Getting back my original stamina will be the real issue over time. I still need to rest several hours during the day, but working out, eating more, and healing up will all help. But generally, I couldn't be happier with the progress so far.

As always, thanks, and I welcome your notes, calls, and solutions for gaining ten pounds in a hurry with a low-capacity digestive system.

———

As a Scout, use optimism to plan out the future of your treatment and tap into your various sources of expertise. In my case, I was fortunate to have a whole team of doctors at Hopkins who were looking at my case from a multidisciplinary perspective. I was optimistic that they would choose the best combination of therapies for me.

Finally, as a Publicist, if you get to that extremely fortunate time when the news is good and you can't resist sharing it with everyone, let the news itself convey the optimism. If the news is bad, convey optimism in terms of the chances of a recovery or the capabilities that may remain.

———

Planting the Flag at the top of Mt. Vaccine

posted by Andrew Trice, Friday, August 15, 2014

Friends:

Don't worry, no news has been good news. Thanks to all of you who have been asking how I'm doing.

It's been four months since the last post, and although I have no plans to clog everyone's inbox again with frequent messages, since we just reached another milestone I thought I had something worth sharing.

Last month, I received the final set of shots from the pancreatic vaccine trial at Hopkins, and earlier today, I had the latest in a series of CT scans that apparently show "stable disease." In other words, no detectable recurrence of the cancer as of yet. The plausible survival horizon continues to extend out. Oh yeah, and I've gained ALL of that weight back. Believe.

Having completed the undergraduate degree in vaccine survival, I will be eligible for the graduate course--more vaccine every six months, if things continue to go well. Enjoy the rest of your summer. Thanks.

5. Proactivity

It's a cliché, but it's true that even if you get tremendous support from everyone around you during the cancer trek, no one is better positioned to look out for your needs than yourself. And this is a critical part of the proactivity tint; you have to be your own advocate with your medical team as well as in your social interactions and in the self-discovery process you undergo.

My favorite personal story about advocacy in medical matters took place was when I was in Crisis Manager mode. The blog entry in the Crisis Manager chapter re-counts how I pressed the medical staff for alternatives to qualify me for the research vaccine--and I was delighted and grateful that they were so willingly creative in help-ing me get there. A humorous instance where advocacy was needed occurred when I was in the hospital and the staff neglected to empty my catheterized urine bag. I was, shall we say, under a lot of pressure when I hit the call bell and kindly demanded relief, but they answered the call and rapidly rectified the situation.

In Scout mode, proactivity could mean taking charge of your army of supporters, as when you are trying to organize a large social event. Prior to my Whipple surgery I want-ed to have a large gathering to feel the support of the many people around me, and luckily for me they were more than willing to be tasked to help me. At the same time, I had to communicate my medical needs and constraints. The whole event gave me a tremendous charge, and you can see some of the background in the following posts.

June 23, 2013: Lotsa Good Feelings, Signup Genuises, and Helping Hands (email)

All:

OK, on to having some fun. As I mentioned in an earlier note, we have been planning a potluck gathering for the weekend before my surgery, and we now have the details confirmed.

This is designed to be a very informal, fun gathering; feel free to simply stop by for a few minutes, come for an early or late segment of the time depending on your schedule or family needs, or stay for the whole time.

We will be coordinating everyone's potluck contributions through a site called SignUp Genius; look for a message/link from C early this week. I tried to cull the SignUp Genius list to those who are reasonably local to the Northern Virginia area, so if you're in that category, are interested in attending, and don't get a message by mid-week, please let me know.

—⚬⚬⚬—

Potluck Location Optimization, and Famous First Words
posted by Andrew Trice, Saturday, June 29, 2013
Thanks so much to R and C for their generosity, flexibility, and hospitality in sponsoring this event!

One request to guests: I think my immune system is in very good shape right now, but as you might expect I am taking some normal, prudent precautions to make sure I am good to go physically for the surgery on Wednesday; that's one of the reasons for having an outside venue for the potluck. I'll be doing my part tomorrow with handwashing and only allowing Sharon to kiss me; likewise if someone in your party is unwell and/or contagious, it may be a good idea for that person to either stay home or keep a little distance.

Thanks so much!

—⚬⚬⚬—

As a Publicist providing your family and friends with health details, proactivity might mean making sure everyone is on board with what's going on and what's expected to happen; as a result, everyone knows their job and is comfortable with it. The following two posts show our attempt to do so.

———∞∞∞———

June 20, 2013: Surgery Day: Request for assistance (email)

Hello all:

I have talked to Sharon at length about what she would like in terms of support onsite at Hopkins and communications to family members and well-wishers on July 3rd. We are hoping and asking for your help along the following lines:

The surgery is Wednesday, July 3rd at 7:30 AM, in Zayed 3rd floor operating area (see attached map for location and parking). Sharon and I will stay the night before up in Baltimore and show up very early on the 3rd for my prep, and we should be able to handle that piece on our own. However, if Mark, Bob, and M could join her later on in the morning for support once the operation is underway, it would be very helpful to her and would give me much peace of mind as well.

Our understanding is that she may get one or two progress reports as the surgery proceeds, and then surgery will be over by early afternoon unless there are unanticipated complications. Once I'm in recovery/ICU and Sharon is informed as to how surgery went, at her discretion those onsite can pass the word along to other family members (probably Mark->Jeff, Bob-->Allison and Elaine, Sharon-->Julia and Laura, but that's all up to you all, I won't know the difference at that time :-)).

Allison, once you get the word from Bob, if you can post that information on the website we're creating I would be most grateful. Don't feel any need to filter or spin the information in any way, I'd like to be as open as possible with everyone as to how things went.

I hope this all make sense -- I'm trying not to overthink things or have a preconceived idea about exactly how things are going to go, just trying to provide a rough frame to start with. And if anyone has particular constraints on this day that we need to work around, by all means let us know. Thanks so much.

—⊷⊶—

Finally, in a more sensitive personal dimension, as a Mortal, you'll find that proactivity is a lot of what the color role is about. It's ironic to say that about a phase when you are "letting go," but think about it: if you are pretty certain you are dying and need to get your affairs in order or say goodbye to people, you've got no choice but to get a move on and make them happen while you're still coherent. Prayer and contemplation alone won't do.

6. Relationships

Managing your relationships is critical in any life phase, and relationships during a cancer trek are no different. Everything from the quality of your care to the extent to which others will fulfill your regular activities will be strongly affected by how those relationships are initiated, developed, and maintained.

You are going to be building many new relationships during the cancer trek (certainly with medical providers, but with others as well), and the strength of these relationships will be a function of how you present yourself to them. You are going to be extending some existing relationships, which will require some work and some vulnerability on your part. And you will need to maintain important long-standing relationships—just because you have cancer doesn't mean you can neglect spouses, family, or old friends. At the risk of sounding a bit crass, playing the "cancer card" with people only gets you so far; we CC's are still accountable for being good to others to the extent of our capabilities. This will require some work and some vulnerability.

As a Publicist, part of your job is to set people at ease and be clear about what is most helpful to you; otherwise you risk getting help you don't want, or conversely, becoming isolated because people feel awkward about your illness and it's safest to just wait and "give you your privacy." And as always, being pleasant and positive to people will pay dividends in both directions.[36]

---

36   This can be overdone. My wife commented to me several times that I presented so much as a "not sick" person even when I was ailing and weak shortly after the surgery that people assumed I was more capable than I was.

Similarly, when you're a Patient, assuming that the staff is there to help you and is genuinely compassionate (even if rushed), can make your experience as positive as possible. Witness this encounter with medical staff during preparation for radiation treatment:

Spa Day down at the CT Donut

posted by Andrew Trice, Thursday, August 29, 2013

So, you thought cancer treatment was all about invasive procedures, heinous side effects, and waiting on pins and needles for test results? Well, that's all part of the game, but there's time to be pampered too.

Consider my experience today at the Hopkins Radiation Oncology facility, where I had a "simulation." The objective of this exercise was to take precise measurements of my body so that the "frickin' laser beams" can be aimed accurately at the tumor margin when I start the actual radiotherapy treatment. Also, they make a foam mold of my trunk area so that I can position my body at the same place each treatment, while resting comfortably without undue stress on my (fat free) backbone.

But the actual experience was surprisingly pleasant. After being allowed to partially and privately disrobe, smiling attendants lead you over to what looks like a massage table. They make the mold by heating up this big piece of foam and then letting you lie in it. Mmmm, soft and warm. Then, they have you sit up and drink some peach-flavored iced tea to ingest the contrast agent--very refreshing. Next, several attractive nurses lovingly place a few marks at strategic locations on your torso for future positioning during the therapy. Finally, you have a CT scan in the body of a gently whirring radioactive donut. I almost fell asleep, it was so relaxing. Done. They lead you out, you try to give them a tip, they politely refuse. (OK, I made up that last part.) (The tip attempt, not the refusal.)

Finally, you have the ability to build incredible relationships through the Guru color role. Anytime you're hurting and don't know what to do, reach out to somebody and offer to help. I've gained so much strength and satisfaction by communicating with my support network verbally and in writing, advising and informing fellow travelers, and participating in fundraising—and received the simultaneous benefits of forgetting about my own distress.

7. *Forgiveness*

At various points on the cancer trek, you're going to be resentful, exasperated, or just plain mad. You feel like you didn't deserve to get this disease, or maybe you do think you deserve it at some level because of prior lifestyle choices. Someone who you thought was going to step up for you simply can't. A nurse misses your vein and has to stick you again. You suffer more pain because you forgot to take one or more of your many pills on schedule. There's a hassle with your insurance. A person makes an inappropriate remark. You miss an event you'd really like to go to because of an appointment or fatigue. The list goes on.

You can't expect to be the center of everyone else's universes, always be perfect yourself, or change the laws of nature. One of the best ways to prepare for disappointment upfront is to cultivate your ability to forgive, on multiple levels.

First, and most obviously, there's forgiving others for things they did or didn't say or do. To not do so risks leaving your relationships embittered. As well-intentioned as people are, they have their own lives going on too—thus the importance of cultivating what I called a "deep bench."

Less obvious, but equally important, is the need to forgive yourself for your physical or emotional reactions to the disease, flaws in your effectiveness at self-care (or applying the color roles!), or lashing out at others in frustration, or any other behavior that is counterproductive. As hard-working and wonderful of a CC as you are, you are going to fall short of your expectations sometimes. It's essential to learn to be gentle with yourself.

The opportunity to forgive yourself comes up most starkly in the Warrior color role. Warrior is not just about soldiering on physically, but keeping up mental or spiritual strength as well. Part of this is letting go of unrealistic expectations of yourself, others, or the course of our disease. Even if there are physical or emotional setbacks or goals you can't reach, self-forgiveness is a powerful tool you can use to move on successfully even in the case of self-perceived failures.

Finally, it's important to forgive the universe or God (if one or both of those constructs are meaningful to you) for inflicting the disease on you. Otherwise you may become burdened with existential baggage you don't need.

The corollary to practicing forgiveness is developing gratitude for the help that you have received, the growth you've experienced, and the blessings you've been given. Even if there are people who can't do as much as you would have wanted, there will also be those who do more than you would have hoped. People you barely know will wish you well and include you in their prayers or just show up out of the blue with food. Thank them all, because it's much easier to forgive when you remember what you have received already. Likewise, acknowledge your own personal growth and any other more mysterious or serendipitous sources of good fortune. You may have the opportunity to express gratitude across many color roles, particularly Actor, Patient, and Publicist.

As a Guru, one way to practice forgiveness is to educate others about what CCs in a similar situation are likely to need and want. I had countless positive interactions with people during my cancer trek, but I also kept hearing about comments that had offended my fellow travelers. I tried to analyze the problem dispassionately and summarize the benefits and risks of different approaches, as shown in the following post:

The Well-Wishers Dilemma: Mincing Around the Cancer Minefield
posted by Andrew Trice, Tuesday, March 4, 2014

One of the things this whole experience has sensitized me to is how challenging it can be to figure out what to say to a cancer patient to be helpful at any given time. Don't get me wrong, you all have handled this with great sensitivity and humor in my case, but I also understand that there can be feelings of awkwardness and helplessness that can make discussing these matters difficult. So, for your consideration (and as always, intended enjoyment), here's my typology of things people can say:

1. Open-ended questions on status, progress, or needs
EXAMPLES:
"How are you feeling?"
"How are the treatments going?"
"When are you done?"
"How can I help?"
"What do the voices tell you?"

UPSIDE: Innocuous and solicitous; leaves space for person to unload, share successes, or tell you what they need.
RISK: Low, except you must be ready to hear unwelcome news and respond to it. But generally a lay-up; if a person doesn't respond well to this approach, they're really having a bad day.

2. Statements of affirmation and encouragement
EXAMPLES:
"You look good."
"You're doing great."
"One day at a time."
"Don't worry, you're going to be fine."
"Just be positive and hope for the best"
"At Disney World, you can do anything if you just believe!"

UPSIDE: Fundamentally a kind thing to say; can create a positive tone, make the person feel good, and provide a positive feedback loop that facilitates healing.
RISK: Low; if the person is feeling down or wants to go to dark places with you, the approach can kind of fall flat.

3. Forging connections by making comparisons
EXAMPLES:
"My _____ had this too, and they ___ "
"Not that it's the same, but I had a similar condition and it was _____ "
"My ___ faced tough odds too, and they did very well"
"Chemo side effects you're describing remind me of my pregnancy experience"
"Gosh, I've had diarrhea before too. Not fun, dude."

UPSIDE: Can have a very empathic effect, inspire, or stimulate an interesting conversation.
RISK: Medium; not good if the comparisons make the person feel discouraged or "one-down" relative to the experience described.

4. Edgy jokes
EXAMPLES:
"No matter what your outcome is, take solace in the fact that you are advancing the cause of science by being a record in an experiment's data table"
"My fatal flaw is laziness; yours is cancer"
"Well, you've still got your health"
Song: "Another One Bites the Dust"

UPSIDE: Humor is a very powerful force.
RISK: Medium to high for most people, very low for me.

5. The Walter White, "Breaking Bad" family approach.
EXAMPLES:
"All I can do is wait....for your cancer to come back."
"Why don't you just die already?"
"You're an insane, degenerate piece of filth, and you deserve to die!"

UPSIDE: Riveting dramatic entertainment
RISK: N/A; I'm not a cold-blooded, brutal meth manufacturer (at least as far as you know).

Finally, for a Mortal, forgiveness is a fundamental part of being able to move on and die with fewer regrets. Hospice nurses report that many patients have an intense need to experience forgiveness at the end-of-life, but the nursing profession does not provide adequate training or interdisciplinary support for this function.[37] Paradoxically,

37 Betty Ferrell, Shirley Otis-Green, Pamela Baird, and Andrea Garcia, "Nurses' Responses to Requests for Forgiveness at the End of Life," *Journal of Pain Symptom Management* 47, no. 3 (2014): 631–41, doi:10.1016/j.jpainsymman.2013.05.009.

another recent study showed that elders who were better at self-forgiveness actually had a lower mortality risk.[38] So why not start forgiving everybody now?

Further Reading on the Tints:

Norman Cousins, *Anatomy of an Illness: As Perceived by the Patient* (New York: W. W. Norton, 1979).

Ruth Levine, *Cancer Warrior: Where the Mind Goes* (Minneapolis: Quill House, 2011).

William Penzer, *How to Cope Better When You Have Cancer*, 2nd ed. (Plantation, FL: Esperance Press, 2012). Probably the best treatment of the tints that I've seen, with extensive sections on optimism, mindfulness, humor, communication, and relationships, among other topics.

Tari Prinster, *Yoga for Cancer: A Guide to Managing Side Effects, Boosting Immunity, and Improving Recovery for Cancer Survivors* (Rochester, VT: Healing Arts Press, 2014). A customized approach to integrating yoga into a cancer wellness program.

---

38   Neal Krause and R. David Hayward, "Self-Forgiveness and Mortality in Late Life," *Social Indicators Research*, 111, no. 1: 361-73.

CHAPTER 14

The Cancer Chameleon Mixes and Morphs: Creating the Best Trek for You

S ome chameleons display so many different colors that it is difficult to character-ize them. Panther chameleons from Ambilobe are kaleidoscopic animals, they can display red, orange, yellow, blue, white and green colors at the same time.[39]

There's only one thing I know for sure about your cancer experience: it isn't going to be the same as mine. Just as each patient's treatment should be customized to the specific characteristics of their disease, each person's strategy for navigating through their cancer trek will require color roles that are different in strength and tint over time. And as we've seen, you'll have to also consider which color roles you can perform yourself and which ones you'll need help with. What is the unique set of pictures you and your support network are going to paint?

Planning and Adjustment Tasks for Your Situation

I call the combination of color roles you need at any given point in time the Cancer Chameleon *mix*, and the changes in mix necessary to respond to a changing situation the Cancer Chameleon *morph*. The individual color roles we've covered in previous chapters represent positive transformations of their own; the mixes and morphs rep-resent a second type of transformation as you move through your trek.

---

39 Millburn, "Identifying a Veiled Chameleon's Color and Mood."

The key is to make it work for you--the mixes and morphs you choose for your palette should feel right and fit your circumstances, flexibility, and temperament. As you progress through your trek continually review your palette by doing one or more of the following interrelated tasks (Fig. 2).

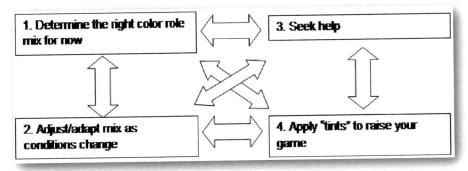

Figure 2: Cancer Chameleon tasks, all interrelated

1) Determine the right color mix for now

Periodically and systematically review your palette and your current situation, and ask yourself whether your *mix* is a good fit for you right now, or for the next change that you foresee along your trek. This doesn't have to be a scientific process; just make a rough assessment of how you're doing on the nine color roles. If the mix seems right and you don't have nagging concerns or any unmet needs or plans, great! You're probably on track.

2) Adjust/adapt mix as conditions change

Whenever you think you may be off track, or perceive that your cancer trek is changing, figure out what the gap is between what you're doing and what you need to be doing; and make the corresponding *morph*. The guide in Table 3 below will give you a sense of what *morphs* you may want to consider to bring things back into balance, based on how you feel it's going for you.

Color Role	Consider doing more if you feel...	Consider doing less if you feel...
Crisis Manager	overwhelmed, distressed, numb	under control, confident, knowledgeable
Publicist	isolated, ignored	the need for privacy, stability
Actor	stigmatized, in need of diversion	the need to focus more on treatment/self-care
Warrior	lackluster, apathetic	burned out, physically okay, ready for hospice
Patient	neglectful of your own care	like a hypochondriac, stigmatized
Scout	Reactive, stuck in "tunnel vision"	"analysis paralysis"
Philosopher	lost, disorganized, scattered, off track	irritated annoyed at your lack of action
Guru	a call to serve others	put-upon, overscheduled
Mortal	too much denial, regret	consumed by dread

Table 3: Indicators of adjustments needed to your CC mix

3) Seek help

Once you know what *morphs* you need to do, ask yourself what help you need to get there. You can't be superb at all nine color roles on your own, especially if your energy is limited, and getting help can also make you a better CC through the relationships you build. Table 4 summarizes the skill sets and type of people and relationships that could help you fulfill the color roles you need assistance with; you can also refer to the individual color role chapters for more details.

Color Role	Needed skill sets, relationships, or help
Crisis Manager	Medical experts, nurse/clinic navigators, advocacy, decision analysis
Publicist	Ghostwriting, advocacy, communications, tact
Actor	Personal services/assistants, normal circle of friends and acquaintances
Warrior	Pain management experts, inspirational fellow travelers
Patient	Nursing/self-care, logistics of care, medical insurance expertise
Scout	Planning, research, analysis, networking

Philosopher	Life coaching, prioritizing/time management, "Great Books" reading
Guru	Leadership training, mentors, volunteers for your cause
Mortal	Estate planning experts, funeral planners, clergy, counselors, hospice workers

Table 4: Summary of Potentially Useful Help With Different Color Roles

4) Apply tints to raise your game

If you feel stuck or depressed, revisit the tints to see if there's a way you can apply those skills or disciplines to improve your situation. Consider adding it on to the color role morphs you feel you need to do. The chapter on tints gives many examples of how they can make the color roles more effective. Ask yourself: Can I deploy any of these to my advantage right now? You are never without options to improve your situation (though it's okay to take five minutes a day to feel sorry for yourself!).

Sample mixes and morphs

Figure 3 below shows a generic collection of mixes and morphs across a hypothetical person's cancer trek. The mixes are read vertically, while the morphs read horizontally. You can see how the proportions of each color role can ebb and flow over time. For convenience, and easy recognition, the color roles are colored the same as in the previous chapters.

A few other notes to keep in mind. First, the height of each color bar represents the proportion of the CC's (or the CC plus their support group's) energy or activity devoted to the color role, not some absolute amount of effort. The physical and emotional energy of the CC during the cancer trek is going to fluctuate; someone in the hospital or recovering from an intense cycle of chemo will clearly have a lot less energy than someone who has been in remission for a while.

Second, the order in which the color roles are stacked has no particular significance (e.g., don't assume that Mortal is the most important just because it is stacked on top.)

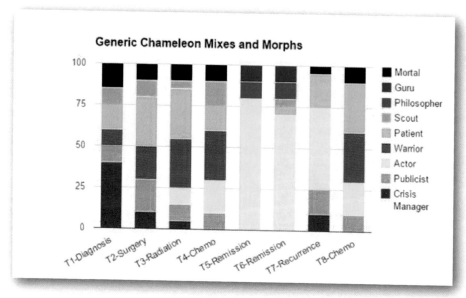

Figure 3: Mixing and Morphing.

Mixes

Again, the *mix* has to do with how you spend your time during a particular phase of the cancer trek. A color role *mix* for a specific time period is represented by one of the stacked bar columns (e.g., T3-Radiation, or the radiation treatment done during time period 3). For the T3-Radiation period mix, notice that the CC is focused on the Patient and Warrior color roles; there's less emphasis on the Mortal, Actor, and Publicist color roles, very little use of Crisis Manager and Scout, and no Philosopher or Guru time at all. This is consistent with a CC going to radiation treatment every day, as there are procedures and appointments all the time (Patient), along with some discomfort and various side effects to bear (Warrior). At the same time, the CC may be worrying about their prognosis (Mortal), doing a few regular activities (Actor), and keeping in touch with well-wishers (Publicist). And the CC may also have a scheduling or transportation emergency or two (Crisis Manager), and plan for a round of upcoming chemo (Scout), but not have any time left to think about how they will change their life priorities (Philosopher) or help out others later (Guru).

Morphs

A color *morph* shows the change in the color role mix over the course of the cancer trek. Notice how the morphs shift depending on the sample CC's circumstances.

When the cancer is first diagnosed (T1-Diagnosis), the CC is typically shocked, overwhelmed, and frightened by the treatments to come and the potential severity of the prognosis, hence the high Crisis Manager and Mortal proportions in the mix; as they move into the more heavy-duty parts of the treatment (T2-Surgery and T3-Radiation), you would expect to see the Patient and Warrior color roles come to the fore, and the Crisis Management and Mortal color roles to recede somewhat, unless the CC is in dire condition.

During the next treatment phase (T4-Chemo), there will be further refinements in the mix because the intensity of the treatments and the CC's reaction to it will be different. If there are periods of remission later on (e.g., T5-Remission and T6-Remission), the CC has the opportunity to do much more regular activity as an Actor and "open up the aperture" on their lives to devote more time to the Philosopher and the Guru. If there is a recurrence (T7-Recurrence), this can trigger more attention to the Crisis Manager and Patient color roles, along with the Publicist needed to update others about the turn of events. Further treatment (e.g., T8-Chemo) may invoke the Patient and Warrior again, and if the condition eventually turns terminal (not shown) you would expect the Mortal color role to increase.

The above is merely illustrative of the mixes and morphs that might occur during a cancer trek, and shows some general patterns (e.g., Crisis Manager usually occurs first and Actor comes to the fore during remission). However, every case will vary depending on the circumstances and personalities involved.

I hope this chapter has given you some ideas on how to apply the mixes and morphs to your situation, and how to move forward if you're feeling stuck or otherwise unsatisfied. In the end, though there is no other way than to learn it by doing it. And cancer tends to be a pretty effective means of forcing you learn, for better or for worse.

CHAPTER 15

Final Thoughts: Cancer Chameleon Expands The Game

*T*he chameleon's ability to change colour evolved not to blend in, but primarily to stand out.[40]

Don't play THE game; play YOUR game, because when you play THE game, the game will play you.[41]

As I've gone through my own cancer trek, I've had two persistent, recurring narratives in my head. One is a nightmare, and the other is a vision.

The nightmare is about the internal enemy—this tumor, this uninvited guest that, even after being ostensibly removed, can later spread and eventually engulf me and take me out. It's the body's version of Hercules' Hydra, the Venus Flytrap in *Little Shop Of Horrors*, the terrorist network of sleeper cells. The dry comment by the radiologist reviewing the CT scan of my abdomen when I was diagnosed captures it best: "The tumor is small, but infiltrative." It's hard to feel safe when you've been infiltrated.

In my worst moments, I visualize the metastasis that could take place in my body-- the cancer's relentless march through multiple system pathways, choking off other

---

40   Ed Yong, "Colour-Changing Chameleons Evolved to Stand Out, Not Blend In," *Not Exactly Rocket Science* (blog), January 29, 2008, http://notexactlyrocketscience.wordpress.com/2008/01/29/colour-changing-chameleons-evolved-to-stand-out-not-blend-in/.

41   J. K., work colleague of the author.

tissues, vital organs, and perhaps life itself, leaving tremendous pain and suffering in its wake. Equally frightening as the toll on the body is its effect on the mind and soul; cancer can choke off the capacity to help others, or the means to do anything "useful" at all. And I go between wanting to fight that with every fiber of my being, and feeling fatalistic in the knowledge that ultimately I may not have control over the course the cancer takes.

But most of the time, I am more preoccupied with a competing vision that transcends any physical toll that cancer can take on me or any of us. And that vision is that as we navigate through cancer, we can experience types of growth other than tumor growth as well. Growth in self-knowledge. Growth in families and relationships. Growth in our thankfulness. Growth in our characters. Growth in scientific knowledge about cancer and how to heal it. Growth in productivity on projects we've been putting off. Growth in our capacity to give and receive love. Growth in our legacies. Growth in our spirits. These are truly forms of "good metastasis" that are possible in the face of cancer, and each of them improves our capacity for healing too, even if the physical outcome of the cancer is not what we want.

Dare I even say it? Cancer is not just a potentially deadly disease; in many circumstances it is an opportunity for personal development.[42] It sounds awful to say this on one level--God knows I am not wishing cancer on anyone. And yet as I look back at my cancer trek, I can honestly say that it has been both the worst time and the best, most meaningful, most social, and most productive time of my life. I hope that this holds true for others as well, and that this book can play some small part in helping you and your loved ones make the most out of the cancer trek that you were so unfairly burdened with.

I said at the outset that I viewed the Cancer Chameleon as a "control system" for navigating cancer. But just as importantly, being a Cancer Chameleon is going to bring forth growth and other positive things in you, your partner, and your support network—things you didn't think possible--because it allows you to play a different game from the one cancer seemingly handed to you. If cancer was a board game, it is as if

---

42   There is some academic evidence to back this up, believe it or not. See, for example, Crystal L. Park, "The Meaning Making Model: A Framework for Understanding Meaning, Spirituality, and Stress-Related Growth in Health Psychology," *European Health Psychologist* 15, no. 2 (2013): 40–7, http://openhealthpsychology.net/ehp/issues/2013/v15iss2_June2013/15_2_Park.pdf.

you are taking a crappy roll and expanding the rules to make them much more favorable to you.

So expand the game board and stand out in the cancer game. You are a Crisis Manager, a Publicist, an Actor, a Warrior, a Patient, a Scout, a Philosopher, a Guru, and a Mortal; but you are also more than any one of these color roles. You are a Cancer Chameleon. You, your loved ones, and your wider support community are going to paint a set of pictures that are uniquely and profoundly yours. And remember the beauty of the path you're on, even when it is difficult. Seize the opportunity, even if "opportunity" is initially about the last word you'd use in connection with your cancer. You'll be very glad you did.

BIBLIOGRAPHY

Allmon, Allison L. Benjamin A. Tallman, and Elizabeth M. Altmaier. "Spiritual Growth and Decline among Patients with Cancer." *Oncology Nursing Forum* 40, no. 6 (2013): 559–65.

American Cancer Society. *Cancer Facts and Figures 2014*. Atlanta: American Cancer Society, 2014. Accessed October 22, 2015. http://www.cancer.org/acs/groups/content/@research/documents/webcontent/acspc-042151.pdf.

Bates, Mary. "How Do Chameleons Change Colors?" *Wired*, April 11, 2014. http://www.wired.com/2014/04/how-do-chameleons-change-colors/.

Bernay, Toni, and Saar Porrath. *When It's Cancer: The 10 Essential Steps to Follow After Your Diagnosis*. New York: Rodale, 2006.

Bone, Roger C. "A Dying Person's Guide to Dying." *Hospice*. American College of Physicians, 1997. Accessed October 22, 2015. https://www.hospicenet.org/html/dying_guide.html.

Chamberlain, Jonathan. *The Cancer Survivor's Bible*. Brighton, UK: Long Island Press, 2012.

Cousins, Norman. *Anatomy of an Illness: As Perceived by the Patient*. New York: W. W. Norton, 1979.

Engber, Daniel. "Is the Cure for Cancer inside You?" *New York Times*, December 21, 2012. http://www.nytimes.com/2012/12/23/magazine/is-the-cure-for-cancer-inside-you.html.

Ferrell, Betty, Shirley Otis-Green, Pamela Baird, and Andrea Garcia. "Nurses' Responses to Requests for Forgiveness at the End of Life." *Journal of Pain Symptom Management* 47, no. 3 (2014): 631–41. doi:10.1016/j.jpainsymman.2013.05.009.

Gawande, Atul. *Being Mortal: Medicine and What Matters in the End*. New York: Metropolitan Books, 2014.

Holland, Jimmie C. *The Human Side of Cancer: Living With Hope, Coping With Uncertainty.* New York: HarperCollins, 2001.

Horner, Christine. *Waking the Warrior Goddess: Dr. Christine Horner's Program to Protect Against and Fight Breast Cancer.* Laguna Beach, CA: Basic Health, 2013.

Johnson, Carolyn. "For Terminal Patients, a Round of Chemo May Be Harmful." *Washington Post,* July 28, 2015.

Kavan, Michael G. Thomas P. Guck, and Eugene J. Barone. "A Practical Guide to Crisis Management." *American Family Physician* 74, no. 7 (2006): 1159–64.

Kivowitz, Barbara, and Roanne Weisman. *In Sickness as in Health: Helping Couples Cope with the Complexities of Illness.* Petaluma, CA: Roundtree Press, 2013.

Krause, Neal, and R. David Hayward. "Self-Forgiveness and Mortality in Late Life." *Social Indicators Research* 111, no. 1 (2013): 361–73.

Krenson, M. Edward. "The Chameleon Principle of Leadership." Randolph School, September 2003. Accessed October 22, 2015. http://randolphschool.net/ftpim-ages/111/download/download_group1501_id23359.pdf.

Kriseman, Nancy L. *The Mindful Caregiver: Finding Ease in the Caregiver Journey.* Lanham, MD: Rowman & Littlefield, 2014.

Lengacher, Cecile Annette, Melissa M. Shelton, Richard R. Reich, Michelle K. Barta, Versie Johnson-Mallard, Manolete S. Moscoso, Carly L. Paterson, et al. "Mindfulness Based Stress Reduction (MBSR(BC)) in Breast Cancer: Evaluating Fear of Reoccurrence (FOR) as a Mediator of Psychological and Physical Symptoms in a Randomized Control Trial (RCT)." *Journal of Behavioral Medicine* 37, no. 2 (2014): 185–95. doi:10.1007/s10865-012-9473-6.

Levine, Ruth. *Cancer Warrior: Where the Mind Goes.* Minneapolis: Quill House, 2011.

Lichtenthal, Wendy, prod. "The Process of Making Meaning from the Cancer Experience." Memorial Sloan-Kettering Cancer Center video, 19:00, 2011. http://www.mskcc.org/videos/process-making-meaning-experience.

Mabuni, Vivian. *Warrior in Pink: A Story of Cancer, Community, and the God Who Comforts.* Grand Rapids, MI: Discovery House, 2014.

Marsh, Jenny, ed. "Finding Your Cancer Cure: Your Basic Guide to Surviving Cancer." Energy Grid: Multi-Issue Alternative Media. Accessed October 22, 2015. http://www.energygrid.com/health/cancer-cure.html.

Melina, Remy. "Chameleon Color Change Isn't All about Hiding." *Live Science,* March 28, 2011. http://www.livescience.com/33159-chameleon-color-change-isnt-all-about-hiding.html.

Millburn, Naomi. "Identifying a Veiled Chameleon's Color and Mood." Pets on Mom. me. Accessed October 22, 2015. http://animals.pawnation.com/identifying-veiled-chameleons-color-mood-5721.html.

Miller, Allie. "Eyes Give 360° Vision: Chameleon." *Ask Nature.* Accessed October 22, 2015. http://www.asknature.org/strategy/f6b73865a35b39d2974e29905e-8b1a8c#.VHx6zRAhC1k.

Miyaki, Nate. *The Way of the Cancer Warrior: 34 Strategies for Your Cancer War.* Nate Miyaki LLC, 2014. Accessed October 22, 2015. http://natemiyaki.com/wp-content/uploads/2014/09/Way_of_the_Cancer_Warrior.pdf.

National Center for Families Learning. "Why Do Chameleons Change Their Colors?" *Wonderopolis.* Accessed October 22, 2015. http://wonderopolis.org/wonder/why-do-chameleons-change-their-colors/.

Nuland, Sherwin. *How We Die: Reflections On Life's Final Chapter.* New York: Random House, 2010. First published 1995 by Vintage Books.

Park, Crystal L. "The Meaning Making Model: A Framework for Understanding Meaning, Spirituality, and Stress-Related Growth in Health Psychology." *European Health Psychologist* 15, no. 2 (2013): 40–7. http://openhealthpsychology.net/ehp/issues/2013/v15iss2_June2013/15_2_Park.pdf.

Park, Crystal L., Ianita Zlateva, and Thomas O. Blank. "Self-Identity after Cancer: 'Survivor,' 'Victim,' 'Patient,' and 'Person With Cancer.'" *Journal of General Internal Medicine* 24, no. S2 (2009): S430–S435.

Pausch, Randy. "The Last Lecture: Achieving Your Childhood Dreams." YouTube video, 1:16:26, from a lecture at Carnegie Mellon University. Posted by Carnegie Mellon, December 20, 2007. https://www.youtube.com/watch?v=ji5_MqicxSo.

Pausch, Randy, with Jeffrey Zaslow. *The Last Lecture*. New York: Hyperion Books, 2008.

Peck, M. Scott. *The Road Less Traveled: A New Psychology of Love, Traditional Values, and Spiritual Growth*. New York: Simon & Schuster, 1978.

Penzer, William. *How to Cope Better When You Have Cancer*. 2nd ed. Plantation, FL: Esperance Press, 2012.

Prinster, Tari. *Yoga for Cancer: A Guide to Managing Side Effects, Boosting Immunity, and Improving Recovery for Cancer Survivors*. Rochester, VT: Healing Arts Press, 2014.

Royal College of Physicians and Royal College of Radiologists. *Cancer Patients in Crisis: Responding to Urgent Needs; Report of a Working Party*. London: Royal College of Physicians, 2012. Accessed October 22, 2015. https://www.rcplondon.ac.uk/sites/default/files/documents/cancer-patients-in-crisis-report.pdf.

Shennan, Christina, Sheila Alison Payne, and Deborah R. Fenlon. "What is the Evidence for the Use of Mindfulness-Based Interventions in Cancer Care? A Review." *Psycho-Oncology* 20, no. 7 (2011), 681–97. doi:10.1002/pon.1819.

Siegel, Bernie. *Love, Medicine, and Miracles: Lessons about Self-Healing from a Surgeon's Experience with Exceptional Patients*. New York: Harper & Row, 1986.

Somerville, Alana. *Chemosabe Cancer Warrior*. Alana Somerville, 2012.

Spiess, Petra. "The Veiled Chameleon (*Chameleo calyptratus*) Purchase and Captive Care." Kingsnake.com. Accessed October 22, 2015. http://www.kingsnake.com/rockymountain/RMHPages/RMHveiled.htm.

Umberson, Debra, and Jennifer Karas Montez. "Social Relationships and Health: A Flashpoint For Health Policy." *Journal of Health and Social Behavior* 51, no. S1 (2010): S54–S66.

U.S. National Library of Medicine and National Institutes of Health, PubMed, http://www.ncbi.nlm.nih.gov/pubmed.

"What Colour is a Dead Chameleon?" *Naked Scientists*, podcast audio, 2:00. December 18, 2011. http://www.thenakedscientists.com/HTML/questions/question/3268/.

Yong, Ed. "Colour-Changing Chameleons Evolved to Stand Out, Not Blend In." *Not Exactly Rocket Science* (blog). January 29, 2008. http://notexactlyrocketscience.wordpress.com/2008/01/29/colour-changing-chameleons-evolved-to-stand-out-not-blend-in/.

Zabalegui, Adelaida, Esther Cabrera, Montserrat Navarro, and María Isabel Cebria. "Perceived Social Support and Coping Strategies in Advanced Cancer Patients." *Journal of Research in Nursing* 18, no. 5 (2013): 409–20.

53186606R00102

Made in the USA
Charleston, SC
04 March 2016